A thanato

Children and young p... ... *perceptions,*
experiences and understanding of
life, death and bereavement

*This book is dedicated to the memory
of
Mark Eveson*

Other books by the same author

Cotton Everywhere
A Northern Thanatology
Thanatology of War

A thanatology of the child:

Children and young people's perceptions, experiences and understanding of life, death and bereavement

by
Christine Kenny

With contributions from
Liz Foster and Margaret Moore

Quay
Books

Quay Books Division, Mark Allen Publishing Group
Jesses Farm, Snow Hill, Dinton, Wiltshire, SP3 5HN

British Library Cataloguing-in-Publication Data
A catalogue record is available for this book

© Christine Kenny 1998
ISBN 1 85642 097 3

Printed in the UK by Cromwell Press, Trowbridge, Wiltshire.

Contents

Acknowledgements

I would like to thank my parents, Ben and Joan Miller, my collegues at South Bank University and Jeremy Weinstein and Tony Leiba for their patience and support during the time that I have spent researching and writing this book; also to Sally and Richard Skillert-Moore for access to participants and to Doreen and Valery Marston.

Special thanks to my children, Lisa, Mark, Leonard and Philip. Thanks also to Liz Foster and Margaret Moore for their contributions and to the people who took part in the study, some of whom are listed below.

Adrian Kearney
Lisa Johns
Paul, Steven and Peter Fish
Marilyn and David Taylor
Mary Morris
Alf Kay
Micheal Powders (known locally as 'Micky Drip' the plumber)
Martin Layland
Stewart Crump
Damian Birtwistle
Melanie Williams
Craig O'Callagan
Tony Fallon
Leonard Miller

Introduction

Personal autobiographies on life, death and dying:

by Christine Kenny and Liz Foster

Much of my writing begins in my head. This chapter began on the ninth floor of Erlang House, South Bank University in London, where I now work. I come here to have a cigarette and admire the view. From here you can see for miles and miles — a view like this reminds you of how good it is to be alive. As a psychologist, my main area of interest is Thanatology, ie. the multidisciplinary study of death, dying and bereavement and, as I studied death and dying, I became increasingly interested in life. Not longevity, that's not the same thing at all. Had I been unduly concerned with my own longevity, I'd have stopped smoking ages ago[1]. A love and value for life has led me to adopt a rather hedonistic philosophy that means, basically, if it gives you pleasure — do it. But, at a deeper level, for me an interest in life indicates an interest in the quality of life; in what makes a good life and in what makes it worth living.

'Thanatology' is rather a sophisticated word to describe this interest in death and dying, an interest that may be considered morbid by some. When we become aware of our own personal mortality, we start to ask questions about life and death. Not everyone makes a career of thanatology in the way I have, but the more we think about death the more, I feel, we seek to find some meaning in life. Young children have no understanding of what death.is, they learn to understand it as they grow older. Understanding the concept of death is the result of different processes, many of which we explore in this book. For most people, this understanding begins with their first experience of a bereavement caused by the death of

---

1   'I am not advocating this perspective, just stating it.'

someone or something significant in their lives. This first encounter with death may be through the loss of a pet, a member of the family or a friend. Usually, although not always, it is caused by the loss of a grandparent. Our first experience of bereavement is usually the most significant, because it brings with it, not only grief, but the knowledge of our own mortality .

My first experience of bereavement came when my grandfather died. I can remember to this day, the sense of numbness and disbelief. I remember the semi-conscious, dream-like state and the logical assumption that 'this is not true, tomorrow I will wake up and everything will be normal.' My grandfather was a short, chunky, darling of a man with a rich, deep northern accent. I loved him dearly. I was eleven years old when he died. A week after his death I had my first menstrual period. This was a significant event that my grandmother put down to the shock. And she was right. For me, the commencement of menstruation signified not just the loss of my grandfather, but a loss of innocence. For our first bereavement is a kind of initiation, a first 'bite' from the tree of knowledge. Our 'fall from grace' comes from the knowledge this brings; an awareness of our own mortality. When my grandfather died, I lost my childhood and became, symbolically at least, a woman. As a woman, I have always carried with me an image of myself as a little girl standing on Rivington Pike[2] with my grandfather. Whenever I think of him, I think of the moors around Bolton. I have said many times 'it's from my granddad that I got my love of the moors.' Yet memory has a strange habit of playing tricks on us, for I never visited the moors with my grandfather. By the time I was old enough and big enough to walk with him anywhere, the lung disease that finally killed him had taken hold. The furthest he could walk (and even then it was with a great deal

---

2   Rivington Pike is one of the highest points in Bolton. From here one can see
Bolton and the surrounding area for miles and miles. It has been a
long-standing tradition in the town that people walk to Rivington Pike on
Good Friday, although these days they frequently cheat and drive as near to
the peak as they can.

of effort) was to Moss Bank Park and back.[3] Yet from his stories I developed a special kind of love for the moors. This was a nostalgic and unrealistic love that stemmed from the images his stories had sketch- ed in my mind. He had grown up on a farm on the moors and it was this, a landscape of the imaginary that I had grown to love. In the months following his death, I looked out to the backcloth of green moors that surrounded Bolton. I had grown up with this image, yet now it took on a new significance. The moors became a special place for me; and in their vast, green splendour, they called out to me. I promised myself that when I grew old enough to explore

them alone I would, and I did. During the years of my adolescence and early adulthood I spent a great deal of time on the moors around Bolton. They really are beautiful; and yet somehow they never measured up to my childhood expectations. Somehow the green was never quite as green, the colors never quite as vivid, as they had been in that sacred place of the imagination that I had painted in the landscape of my mind. The moors of the real, and of the imaginary, did have one thing in common; the colour green. Green, a soothing colour that signifies a strange sadness; the kind that comes from becoming resigned to that which we cannot change.

---

3   Moss Pank Park was about ten to fifteen minutes walk away from my Grandparents house in Bolton.

As I grew older, this image changed becoming not one image but two. In my fantasies they displayed a strange interplay; 'me looking at me.' Whenever I experienced a stressful period in my life, the two images would drift into each other in my fantasies and dreams; sometimes appearing separately, sometimes superimposed. Finally, I felt a need to paint it, to reproduce it in some medium 'out of me' so that I could read it and try to understand it. I called the painting 'here's looking at me: one and two.' I decided to include a short discussion of this image in this book, because I feel that many people can relate to its symbolism. That is the irony of our lives; we spend our childhood wishing we could grow up and be independent, only to find that, when we do, independence brings responsibility. In general, the majority of people adjust quite well to the responsibilities of adult life; we make the best of it. Despite this adjustment, there is always a sense of loss for the child we were; the carefree child who could depend on others, who left all the worrying to the adults. This child that we were, is, ironically, the child who felt that he or she would surely burst if the little adult inside had to wait any longer to get out. And who was the little adult? The one who would make its mark. The one who, as it became increasingly aware of death, became increasingly determined that its life would count for something. Years later, the little adult, liberated at last from its childhood 'cage' looks back and asks, 'Well what was it all for?' Cynicism grows, stemming from the cruel knowledge that things are not always as they seem.[4]

I thought I was the only one to think like that. How wrong I was. When I started my research on Bolton life, nearly eight years ago, I found that many of the people I interviewed, experienced similar thoughts, fears and longings. I gradually came to the conclusion that everyone wants to find some meaning to life and the main reason for this is we know that we will, eventually, die.

---

4   For me one example of this came with the knowledge as a I grew older that the one thing about my grandfather which I had found most comforting, the kind of 'edge' he had to his breathing, was caused by the lung diseases that finally killed him.

For me, the most interesting thing about conducting research is the help it gives in understanding the shared 'common ground'. In finding this common ground, we develop a love and respect for other people. This does not mean that we love everyone we come in contact with, but it does mean that we can learn to love the humanity we all share. This book started with a series of interviews with older persons and their experiences of working in the textile industry. I wrote my first book from the data this research yielded, but it did not cover all the issues raised during the interviews. One common theme to emerge was that of illness, death and dying. I decided that this data could be used to produce another book on death and dying and from there the project expanded. The earlier interviews were followed up by further interviews with young people and adults (20 in addition to the original sample of fourteen women). In the beginning, I did not intend to interview young people. However, friends of my teenage children discovered I was writing about life and death and, one evening in 1996, a group of us started talking.[5] Research is as much about taking advantage of a good opportunity as it is about planning. That night I took out a tape recorder and recorded the discussion.

Further interviews followed and most of the young people interviewed have followed the progress of the research with as much enthusiasm as my co-authors and me. The interviews yielded some astonishing data. All but one of the young people interviewed are unemployed and most have never had a job. They are a group of young people who appear to have little prospects and who lack any formal further or higher education. Yet despite all the odds stacked against them, they have managed to impose some meaning on their lives, a meaning that has more to do with being, than with doing. The young people interviewed were told that the aim of the book was to provide adults and professional people who have responsibility for young people with some insight about how children and young people come to understand death,

---

5   The initial interviews began as one focus (or group) interview with two of my teenage children and four of their friends.

how they place meaning to the experience of bereavement and how their ideas about death can shape their ideas about life. They were also told that the intention of the book is to provide some guidelines on how best to support children and young people who experience a bereavement. They responded to my request for help with interest and enthusiasm. Soon, I had gathered data from 20 young people and adults, aged between 18–23 years of age (16 young men and four young women). A further fifteen adults between the ages of thirty and sixty years of age (five women and ten men) also agreed to take part in the study. Six were interviewed and a further nine filled in an open-ended questionnaire. The insights that the participants in the study gave me and my co-authors have been so revealing, moving and at times, even humorous, it would be impossible for me to express in words the sense of gratitude that I feel towards them. I hope that in writing this book, my colleagues and I have done the testimonies justice. I also hope that the book will prove to be of practical use and that, finally, it will promote a more positive image of the kind of young people who took part. The young people who took part in this study may be unemployed and may lack prospects, but they are certainly not lazy and unthinking.

The project has grown and indeed is still growing. I continually gather more data, especially on experiences of bereavement during the war years. To make the best use of the data collected, we have drawn on theory, because many of the theories of child development are useful in helping us to understand ourselves, our acquaintances and our children a little better. Many psychologists are interested in the grieving and bereavement process and the theories they have developed have enabled us to better understand and support the bereaved. Death rituals and the ways in which people express their grief differ across time and cultures. But symptoms, such as numbness, anger, denial and pining are, in general, expressed by the bereaved (Parkes, 1970; Bowlby, 1979; 1980). Grief is a very painful experience and, because of this, it is not unusual for us to engage in different strategies, designed to help us 'hang on' to the person we have lost. This book is concerned with children and young people's experiences and perceptions of death, dying and bereavement but, in talking about these topics, they spoke also of the different meanings, which life holds for them. Although, we have drawn on theory where relevant, we have tried to keep theoretical concepts to the minimum, allowing the 'voices' in these pages to 'speak for themselves.' Should readers wish to follow up this book with further reading on bereavement, a bibliography and reference list is included at the back.

Liz Foster

When Christine invited me to contribute my own experiences of bereavement, I was pleased to be given the opportunity of pouring out on paper, feelings that I had wanted to share — quite a self-indulgence. What is significant, is the difficulty I had in identifying with much of what was said by those interviewed in the book. My experience was so different and I found it hard not to envy those who were able to talk so freely about a subject which, in my family, has always been shrouded in secrecy.

Far removed from the northerners who share their experiences in the book, I am the only daughter of a genteel woman descended from Leicestershire farming stock. Born in 1919, many of her values seemed more appropriate to the Jane Austin world of the late eighteenth century. She betrayed little emotion and rarely spoke of illness and death. I was five years old when my grandmother, who lived near us on the outskirts of Derby, died. I remember eavesdropping as my mother spoke to her cousin on the telephone and awkwardly uttered the word 'cancer'. There was no mention of the funeral. I was completely protected from anything to do with death and dying. My grandmother was never mentioned again and it was as if she had never existed.

In adult life, my next involvement with death and the first funeral I attended was that of my father. As with my grandmother, my mother never referred to him again. The saddest secret, and one I have only just discovered as I sorted papers following my mother's death, is that she had borne a baby boy who lived for just one month. Two years later, I was born, but I never knew of the brother I might have had. How much silent grief she must have suffered and how resolutely she must have determined not to respond to my childish questioning about why I was an only child. Fifty years after his death, I have had a headstone put in the churchyard where records show him to be buried.

Christine gathered the three of us together to produce this book, to raise awareness of the need for bereaved children to have appropriate support systems that are sensitive to their needs. I can only applaud her commitment to heighten the profile of this area, which is so vital to mental well-being.

Children's experiences of bereavement

We begin this book with a discussion of children's experiences of death and bereavement and an exploration of how they assign meaning to such experiences. The people interviewed for this study have provided excellent material for the book. All of the older and younger people interviewed were very articulate and expressed their feelings and thoughts with such insight and eloquence that we felt it would be wrong to edit them too much. To do such a thing would deny the reader a chance to share the stories. For this reason, we have included large sections of the transcript material gathered for the study, together with a limited analysis by the authors.

In the working-class communities of Bolton, it has been usual to include children in caring practices and death rituals. This means that children have developed a familiarity with the community spirit generated by a funeral (Roberts, 1989; Kenny *et al*, 1998a). This custom of including children in death rituals appears to be characteristic of working-class life in Bolton. Most of the older and younger people who took part in the study expressed a belief that children should be encouraged to attend funerals of the people for whom they cared.

"I think that children should attend, I think it's better, it helps them to come to terms with it and it's a social event too (laughs). I know that sounds morbid but in a way it is. It's a way of getting some support and you get the chance to talk about the person who's died, which is nice for those close to whoever it is that's dead and you can get the chance to have a laugh sometimes. The thing is a funeral can be an enjoyable thing sometimes, in a daft kind of way. You'll often get people laughing as well as crying at a funeral and I think that's good, I don't think it does any harm if people have a laugh at a funeral. We all have our funny little ways and I think, well, if people had a little laugh and chuckle at us while we are alive why not when we are dead? That's all part of remembering that person.

And I think that children need to understand that, that people may die but they live in the memory of others, the memory of them that is.

If children miss the funeral they miss everything else. So how else can they get to understand these things. How can I say it . . . it gives them like a perspective on the matter. Death is frightening, if we are honest none of us want to die. But at the end of the day it's coming to us all so we need to get used to the idea — well as used to the idea as will ever be and not get sort of overcome by it. Children need to understand that OK no one wants to die but its not that terrible. Well it is but it's not if you see what I mean. Children are just like anyone else, they need to get it in perspective. And anyway, why should children be excluded? I think its good for them. Good in the sense they need to know about death and, to be honest, I think that it's more frightening for them if they are excluded. Because you know what kids are like, if you don't include them, well they imagine all sorts of things...yes I definitely think its better."

The idea expressed by the speaker above that people can retain some life in the memory of others is similar to the Hebrew Old Testament view. This perspective does not embrace any belief of an after-life. However, a dead person's spirit can live on in the memory of the tribe (Pojman, 1992). Several of the people who took part in this study spoke of the value of talking about the deceased. For some, talking was a way of keeping the dead person alive by 'willing' or 'speaking into being' a spiritual presence. For others, it represented a way of taking this even further into a communication with the dead person, and some explained that talking was a way of paying tribute to the dead person. Whatever the reason given for talking about the deceased, there was an implicit suggestion that talking gave the living power to summon forth a tangible essence of the deceased. The young man quoted below talks of a friend of his who had died a few years ago. The young man and other friends meet every year on the anniversary of their friend's death. On these occasions, they talk about the times they had shared with him.

"It's a way of keeping him alive really. It was very hard for us when he died because he was our age group like, and you think of death being something that only happens to old people. We were really shocked when he died and angry really. We were angry because it was so unjust I mean, he'd not lived his life and we really found it very hard to deal with. It also made us realise that it could happen to us. We meet every year on the anniversary of his death and we don't do a lot, we just talk. But it's funny when we talk about him it's as if he is still here. He died five years ago now and when we talk about him, it's really funny but it's as if he is with us, as if we really have brought him back just for that one night. It really upsets you when someone of your own age dies. His mother let us go to the funeral and we were all very grateful to her for that. We did the same at his funeral, you know. Just talked about all the daft things we did with him. And it was then that we decided, me and his other mates that we would do this, you know, meet up every year and talk about him. This way we are sort of helping to keep him alive . . . the memory of him that is."

Other respondents expressed gratitude to adults who had included them in death rituals, such as viewing the body and attending the funeral. In this chapter we are concerned with the emotional impact a child's first encounter with death can have. Like the young man quoted above, the woman below expressed her gratitude to the bereaved parents of a friend who died when she was young

"The first funeral I attended would be when I was about six or seven years old and a girl at school had 'died' of rheumatic fever. She was about thirteen or fourteen but attended the same school. Her mother let all the school children go to look at her. We filed up the stairs of her home where she was laid on the bed. I thought she looked like 'Snow White'. Then on the day of the funeral all of the school children went into church and sang a hymn for her. Her best friend walked between her mum and dad and carried a bunch of lilies. For a long, long time I wondered where she had really gone to. Again I never truly found the answer."

The extracts above have been taken from the transcripts of a young man aged 23 years and an older woman aged about 70 years. There are some similarities. Both, for example feel grateful that they had been invited to the funeral and both suggest that they are searching for an answer to what happens after death. The young man considered that it was important to keep the memory of his dead friend alive by talking about him. When asked about his religious views, he insisted that he believed in some form of life after death but was unsure about what form this afterlife would take. He was unsure about life after death or reincarnation and so, too, were most of the other young people interviewed.

The older woman is affiliated to the Spiritualist Church. For her the existence of a life after death appears more certain. The woman's quotation comes from her response to the questionnaire used. The reader may have noted that in her response, the woman put the word 'died' in quotation marks. This is probably because of the spiritualist belief that no one really dies but rather moves on to another plane. However, in her concluding sentence, there is still some sense of uncertainty because she writes that, although she always wondered where her dead friend had gone, she had never found out.

When the author began her interviews she expected to find great differences in the responses to her questions between the older and younger groups. But there were, in fact, far fewer variations that could be attributed to age differences than she had anticipated. The older group reported more experiences of viewing a body in the home of the deceased. However, some younger people also spoke of these experiences. So clearly some parents, at least in Bolton, do include children in funeral and death rituals. Differences in reported responses to such experiences seem to have been due to a variety of factors other than age and include the child's personality. The child's level of intellectual development is also important and we discuss this in *Chapter 2*. The woman quoted above realised that children can perceive and thus experience a death very differently from adults; but she also drew attention to the role of adults (and the way that children perceive them) in shaping such experiences. The woman continued her interview by discussing the death of two of her aunts.

'When I was thirteen, two of my favourite aunts 'died' within a few months of each other, both with cancer. These were two funerals I did attend and was very, very upset, in fact everyone was. Relatives kept saying that they were only 53 and 45 respectively but when you are thirteen you think that is ancient.'

The Bolton custom of including children in death rituals and funerals contrasts with (what is alleged to be) the current trend, in which adults protect children and young people from anything connected with death and dying (Finke *et al*, 1994). This is despite the fact that many health professionals consider children should be told about death and be made to feel secure in their bereavement (Hughes, 1995). Gorer (1965) found in his research on contemporary attitudes towards death that little over a third of the 126 people who took part in his study had children under sixteen years of age. Over half of these had not told their children anything at all about death and dying. Others admitted that when discussing death with their children they used euphemisms such as 'gone to heaven' or 'gone to Jesus.' Gorer concluded that:

'Traditionally, British parents find it embarrassing to talk to their children about subjects of deep emotional importance, and traditionally they tend to hide their own deep emotions from their children's observations.'

Gorer also noted that:

'It is difficult to avoid the conclusion that a sizeable number of British parents are using God and Jesus in communication with their children in exactly the same way that they use Santa Claus, as fairy tale figures'.

(Gorer, 1965)

However, writers such as Wells (1990) stress the importance of recognising the individuality of every child and caution against making generalisations. Another of the young people interviewed for example, reported that he was pleased that his parents had protected him when he experienced bereavement for the first time when his grandfather died.

"The first death I ever came across was when my granddad died. I can't say that my parents and that were dead honest with me but then in another way they were. Like they told me that my granddad had gone to heaven and was with Jesus. As a matter of fact they wasn't being dishonest with me because both my parents and grandparents believed in God so as far as they were concerned that actually was the truth. They didn't invite me to the funeral and I'm not sure what I think about that. In one way I think it was better. I don't think that at that age I'd have understood any better. I mean I did have problems understanding that he would never come back. I remember that quite clearly, you know I kept on asking when would my granddad come back. But I was only about seven years old, well a child of seven can't really understand what you mean by 'never'. I think it was better that they sort of protected me until I was old enough to understand. I'm glad they did it and I agree with them and to be honest I'll do the same with my kids, you know if someone dies and I don't think they are ready to deal with it then I'll protect them. I think it can go too far all this including kids in everything. I don't think its fair. A child shouldn't have to take on board any more than they can understand and deal with. It's not fair to expect more from them than they can understand."

If we accept the view of writers such as Wells, and the young man quoted above, it could be considered that people like Gorer are being rather hard on parents who use euphemisms. In *Chapter 2* we discuss how children differ in their ability to understand the concept of death due to a variety of issues, such as their age and level of intellectual development. It may be that some of the people who responded to Gorer's survey may have been responding to their children's questions about death in the best way that they could, by coming down to the child's level. It is also important to consider that when some parents tell their children that the deceased has gone to God or to heaven, this is what they believe, a point made by the young man cited above. Religion clearly has quite an influence on people's beliefs about death and of what happens after it. This point comes across very clearly in the quotation cited below, taken from a transcript of one of the older men interviewed.

"Being Roman Catholic, I was told that at school, that when we die we go to Jesus and Mary in heaven. We never had any choice about what to believe, this is what we were told and this is all we ever believed. I believe it now, why should I question it. I pray every night that I'll get up at six in the morning and I get up at six in the morning. So why should I question it?"

However, Gorer found that the parents who responded to his study used religious euphemisms regardless of whether they were religious or not. Gorer conducted his work in the 1960s. Since then, there have been many changes in people's ideas about what children should be told about death. Indeed, many of the innovations in practice discussed in our concluding chapter developed as a response to the widespread belief that children in western society are over-protected from the knowledge of death. The limited data collected for this book does not allow generalisations to be made about what kind of beliefs are dominant in Bolton in relation to this issue. But there is still a lot of literature and research to support the view that children are generally still shielded from death. The problem is that there are no 'foolproof' prescriptions to tell us what is best for an individual child.

One of the contributors, Margaret Moore remembers how she felt shocked when she came to this country and found that children were excluded from funerals. Margaret recalls that, in Jamaica, children are included in all aspects of life and death. Later, working as a nurse at Great Ormond Street Hospital, she remembers experiencing considerable ambivalence when she worked with bereaved parents. She found on such occasions that in some ways her British self had assimilated the view that bereaved parents should exercise some self-control, at least in public. But her Jamaican self rebelled, signalling to her a belief that bereaved parents should be allowed the freedom to express their grief publicly.

We are all individuals whose behaviours and perceptions vary according to the contexts in which we find ourselves. Consideration of the best way to support the bereaved varies even in the same individual. Most of the older women interviewed had vivid childhood memories of their experiences of bereavement. They explained that it was once common for people to die and be laid out at home. Most of the older women interviewed had experiences of laying someone out and remembered how common it was for households to have a laying out drawer in which the laying-out set (ie. white night-dress, socks, soap etc) was kept.

"Yes, when I was young most people died at home, it was very few who died in hospital. My grandma, my granddad and my aunt Jane all died at home with their family around them. And when they knew that someone was dying, I can't explain it but there was a great sense of calm. They accepted it when someone was dying, there was no panic. I mean my Aunt Jane was only 30 when she died and I can remember my cousin was playing on the bed. He would be about six months old and he dropped his dummy and she, my aunt Jane, just handed it to him. And you know they all knew that it very unlikely that she would last the day. But no one thought that a child of that age shouldn't be there at six months, that he was in the way. He was one of the family and he had as much right to be there as anyone else. And there was no question of shipping her away because she was dying. Things went on as normally as possible. And when they died, they (the family) immediately washed them, the family did the washing, there was a drawer, a laying out drawer where everything was kept. There used to be long white stockings, there used to be this long white night-shirt and everything used to be white. And they used to put this thing on their heads. And every home had a laying out set, what they called the laying out set, and a towel, they would try to use, a brand new towel if they could. And everything used to be there for the laying out, and they used to wash them and put all clean sheets on the bed, clean pillow cases, and I was never afraid of a dead body.'

It is interesting to consider the similarities between the everyday account of death given above and the practice of people from other cultures. Laungani's account of death in a Hindu family is of particular interest because we have a large

Hindu community in Bolton. In his discussion of a typical Hindu funeral, Laungani (1997) places emphasis on the importance of members of the bereaved family laying-out the deceased. Once again there are strong similarities with accounts given by older people interviewed for this study, on funeral practises in Bolton. This is similar to how things once were in Bolton. Another similarity with traditional practices in Bolton is the way all family members are included and the general sense of 'homeliness' in the death scenes described. Below we cite Laungani's description of the type of gathering of friends and family in the house of the deceased that might be expected in a typical Hindu funeral:

'The body lies on a sheet on the floor, and is covered by a thin white cotton sheet. The face is drained of all colour, and in rigour, remains uncovered. The mourners who have just arrived, sit cross-legged on the floor beside the body, their palms joined in silent prayer. Despite the overhead ceiling fan which whirls monotonously, the heat is quite overwhelming. Some mourners fan themselves with newspapers and in doing so disturb the flies that have settled on the deceased's uncovered face. A few cry openly, tears streaming down their eyes. A few mumble prayers, reciting slokas from sacred religious texts. They all gaze at the inert body in intense sorrow. An elderly woman, who it turns out, is the sister of the deceased and has only just arrived from Deli, wails disconsolately until she is led away gently by the rest of the members of the family. Occasionally a child wanders into the room, and stands to watch. No one attempts to turn the child away. The child, bewildered and intimidated by the large group crowded in the room, scampers away'.

(Laungani, 1997)

There are differences as well as similarities in the ways in which funerals are conducted in Bolton and Laungani's account of funeral practices in India. For example, even now in some families, it has been the tradition for people to visit the house of the deceased to view the body, which was usually placed in an open coffin. In houses that had a front parlour, it was usual for viewing to take place in this room. Just before the funeral procession leaves the house, the lid is placed on the coffin. Laungani writes that in India, the body is transported to the crematorium in an open frame with the corpse open to public view. In both the cultures described, it is usually male members of the family who carry the frame or coffin bearing the deceased. In a typical Irish wake and a Hindu funeral, it is usual for the men to take the body to the cemetery or crematorium while the women and children of the family remain at home. So, although in both Irish and Hindu funerals it is considered appropriate to include children in the funeral there are limits as to how far this involvement should go. Gender also influences the funeral practices of many cultures. For example, one man interviewed is quoted below discussing the Irish wake:

> *"Over there (in Northern Ireland) the women and children stay at home while the men go to the cemetery, there's no women or children go there now. And they don't take part in the wake as such. The women and children sit in one room, and the women, they like, make the sandwiches and the tea and the men sit in the other room and have the wake."*

The respondent cited above has not lived in Northern Ireland for many years and, since his move to Bolton, admitted that a number of his own views had been modified significantly, including those on gender appropriate behaviour. It appears that this was done with a little help from his wife who was also interviewed and is quoted below:

> *"Of course he went along with all this (ideas about gender) before he met me. He was a male chauvinist pig before he married me (both laugh) but I have had to educate him. Thanks to me he is no longer a male chauvinist pig."*

The two extracts above are taken from the transcript of a husband and wife interview. This was quite a relaxed and humorous event, as readers may gather from the light-hearted nature of the material presented. Yet the female respondent makes some valid points. She has noted, for example, that social and religious practices are often modified to fit different social contexts. In Bolton, women have tended to work in paid employment, regardless of marital status due to the textile industry. This has had a 'knock on' effect on family life so that husbands and children have had to share at least some responsibility for the task of running the home. Children in the working-class communities of Bolton have often taken responsibility for duties, such as looking after younger siblings and, therefore, have been included in many areas of what might be considered the adult arena. This may be one reason why it has been the practice to include children in death rituals. Now that many Bolton people are adopting more middle-class values and lifestyles it will be interesting to see what effect, if any, this has on the involvement of children in funerals.

Laungani makes similar points in his 1997 paper on the Hindu funeral when he stresses the diversity of such practices. India's population consists of people from a variety of religious affiliations, within which there are numerous interpretations of how funeral practices should be carried out. He also points out the need to consider ways in which religious practices change over time and place. For example, Laungani makes some interesting observations about the ways British Hindus have modified funeral practices, partly to fit in with British law and partly to fit in with their own changing beliefs and values.

Roberts (1989) argues that it is very important for us to have a knowledge of children's experiences of death rituals in the past because such knowledge can help to inform current practice. This information can enable us to educate children about death in more appropriate ways. It can also inform us about ways in which bereaved children can be supported. Her oral history research centred in the North of England, revealed that, in the past, children were exposed to death from a very early age. She also found that children would sometimes need to take responsibility for dealing with the practicalities of organising the funeral.

Roberts tells a story recited by one of her respondents. The older woman concerned remembered that, when she had been about nine to ten years of age, she had had to dispose of the tiny corpse of her baby sibling. The woman's mother had been too ill following delivery of her stillborn child to deal with funeral, so she had asked her daughter to place the tiny corpse in a shoe box and to take it to the local cemetery. Here, the grave digger agreed to place the tiny package in the next open grave.

At the present time funerals are generally expensive and lavish, so that many readers may consider such a 'cheap' funeral (particularly of a child) to be quite appalling. But it is surely clear to anyone who reads Robert's paper that, although very basic, the funeral of the stillborn child was conducted with much feeling, respect and tenderness. Readers may also consider that it was rather harsh for a young girl of nine to have to take responsibility for the burial of her sibling. However, we have already discussed in this chapter that many children like to be involved in funerals. The respondent interviewed by Robert's appeared to take great pride in describing the way that she had dealt with the responsibility. So it is possible that we underestimate children. However, there is also evidence to suggest that adults in the recent past did not always take what children said very seriously, perhaps putting some things down to 'childish' imagination. One respondent who took part in this study, for example, explains that a vision she had of her late grandmother was 'fobbed off' by adults:

"I was three years old when my grandmother who had always lived with us passed away after a long illness. I always went in to see her every morning. When the morning came that she passed, they didn't know that I had gone into her myself until I said 'grandma is asleep and won't talk to me this morning.' Not very long after this, I was in my little bed and I saw her face in a beautiful halo of light in the corner of room. I was frightened and kept saying that grandma was in the corner of the room. They tried to fob me off that I was dreaming but I knew that I was awake when I saw her. In fact I can still see that halo of light and her face to this day. It definitely wasn't a dream."

The woman quoted above remained firm in her belief that she had seen this image of her grandmother even in adult life and indeed, is a member of the Spiritualist Church in Bolton. To what extent this early experience influenced her adult affiliation with the Spiritualist Church she did not discuss.

Not all of the respondents interviewed by Robert's or indeed for this study had such a matter-of-fact attitude to their first encounters with a death. One respondent did not want to discuss his first attendance at a funeral in any depth at all. When asked what he had felt like at his first funeral, he abruptly responded with the words 'awkward, unsure.' Another when asked 'do you remember the first funeral you attended', answered with bare details but did not go on to discuss her understanding or feelings on the occasion:

"I remember going with other pupils to the funeral of one of our numbers who had been killed on the road."

Some people, regardless of age, do not wish to view the body of the deceased because they feel that it may interfere with their memories of them in some negative way, as the woman cited below recalls:

"When my granddad died I went over to my grandmother's house to pay my last respects. His body was in the front room and quite a lot of relatives were going in to say a last goodbye and to have a last look at him. My grandma asked if I would like to see him and I said 'no.' She was very good about it, I mean, I know that she probably thought that seeing him was the right thing to do but she didn't insist that I go along with it (viewing the body). She never pressured me and she respected my wishes that I did not want to see him. I wanted to remember my granddad as he was in life, as I had known him. I wanted to remember the granddad who had thrown me up in air when I was little, who had joked with me and tickled me . . . even the granddad who could be a grumpy old soul at times, but you know, all of things that he had been to me in life. I really couldn't face the idea of seeing that nice old man, or when he was in a mood, that not such a nice man, who had always been so lively and had always been there all through my life, lying dead in a coffin. I really could not have tolerated that."

When we consider the extract above, it is useful to recall the point made by Wells (1990) that every child responds to death in their own individual way. It is clear that the woman concerned had no desire to see her grandfather's body. Yet we can infer from her recollection of the event that she has progressed through the stages of grief quite well. The woman gave her story with obvious sadness at having lost her grandfather, but nevertheless she spoke of the experience quite easily. She also had a realistic memory of her grandfather, remembering his good as well as his bad points. For example, the fact that he could be grumpy at times. In other words, the woman did not remember an 'idol' who could do no wrong, but rather, a human being.

Reactions to viewing a corpse also appear to be influenced by the support the child received and the attitudes to death of the adults present. This point is well illustrated in an extract presented below. This has been taken from the transcript of an older Bolton woman (aged 65 years) who spoke of her experience of viewing her grandmother's body:

Chris Kenny: *Could you tell me about the first dead person you ever saw?*

Storyteller: *It was my grandmother. I was ten years old and I came out of school and I was staying with my aunt X at the time and she met me outside school, and she said, 'Your grandma is dead, your grandfather wants to see you.' So I went, and she'd been washed and everything, and all the bedding was clean and there was this white counterpane on the bed, which came as a bit of a shock to me because prior to this there had been a colourful counterpane on. Well, she had a sheet over her face and my granddad said, 'You must come to say good-bye to your grandma now.' And I said, 'No, no I don't want.' And my granddad said 'There is nothing to be frightened of,' and he said, 'Was you afraid of your grandma when she was alive?' and I said, 'No.' He said , 'Well then, there is nothing to be afraid of now.' So*

> *he took the sheet back and I was amazed at the beauty of her, I mean, she was only 62 when she died, and there wasn't a wrinkle on her face and she had a lovely complexion, and she had white hair. Her hair was naturally wavy at the front, and they (the family) had washed her and set her hair, and she had been prepared with love, and she had this white nightie on, and I realised that there was nothing to be frightened of with a dead body. To me she just looked like she was sleeping, and dead bodies never frightened me after that.'*

The woman cited above recalls that she was about ten years of age when the event described above took place. There are several issues to consider when we relate this to the discussion in *Chapter 2*. Here we discuss the way children's emotional and intellectual development can shape their perceptions of and responses to a bereavement. In this chapter, we have focused our exploration on how children of different ages have different needs in relation to the type of appropriate support they need when they encounter death (Furman, 1964; Finke *et al*, 1994). In relation to the extract above, several points are worth noting. First there is attention to detail, eg:

> *"and there was this white counterpane on the bed, which came as a bit of a shock because prior to this there had been a colourful counterpane on."*

When exposed to the sight of a corpse for the very first time, several writers have commented on the 'waxy' appearance of the skin, the 'whiteness'. This observation is quite accurate. The skin of a dead person generally does have a waxy appearance in the first few hours following death. One of the authors, a former nurse, recalls that many people want to comment on this appearance when they encounter a corpse for the first time. It is not so much the observation in itself that is of interest, but the various ways in which people can respond to it; fearfully, with disgust or with curiosity. The author also recalls a discussion she once had with a young doctor.

The doctor concerned had only recently completed medical school. He had been called out to certify a death on the hospital ward on which the author was working. This young doctor was fascinated by the 'waxiness' and 'whiteness' of the corpse. His response was to describe his observation in medical and biological terms. According to him, it was a fascinating issue to be discussed and explained in objective medical terminology. But the 'objective' attitude adopted by the young man may well have been a coping strategy to deal with the experience. The strange thing is that this appearance gives the corpse an aura of mysticism. Human, yet not quite human. A kind of mannequin, so lifelike in appearance that it promises to open its eyes to speak to you at any moment. The author recalls her ambivalence when she handled a corpse shortly after death. This mannequin effect softened her heart and served as a reminder that here was the symbol of a human being. Yet there was also an element of fear, not from any superstition that the corpse might cause actual harm but more a kind of awe. For in its still, white and 'deathly' counsel, the silence of the corpse represented a kind of privileged and puritanical knowledge. Now she/he knows, and we do not. For the author, this wisdom was fearful, touching and sacred.

One of the male respondents, a forensic pathologist, also commented on his experience of the way in which doctors tend to objectify a corpse. This tendency to objectify the corpse may reflect part of a medical 'hidden curriculum'.[1] It was an approach with which the forensic pathologist strongly disagreed. During his interview, he spoke of his recognition of the humanity of the corpse. It is this essence of humanity in a human corpse and sensed by some individuals, which brings home the fact that it represents a human life and one that has ended. No matter how expected or even 'desirable' the death may be (the deceased may have suffered from a distressing and even painful illness), if we accept the assumption that every human life is precious, the end of every human life is surely a tragedy. Our perception of this tragedy will influence our

---

1   We have to be careful of course, and avoid the assumption that all doctors perceive the corpse in this way.

response to viewing a corpse. Not everyone recognises the humanity in a corpse. When they view a dead body, they do not see the person they knew in life, but rather an empty shell. This was the case for a man in his late thirties who was interviewed and is cited below:

> *"I never viewed my granddad when he died, I never wanted to. I did see my grandma when she died, but I didn't find it helpful at all, I didn't really see that it was her really; she didn't look the same. She was the first and very last dead person I ever saw. I never did it again ... I just don't see the point in it to be honest.'*

The young man describes an experience that is very different from that cited by the older woman who spoke of viewing her grandmother. But when we go back to her account and contrast it with the extract above, it appears that each respondent is viewing the corpse through a very different lens. For example, the woman did not focus on the whiteness of the corpse alone. She spoke of the bedspread and how its whiteness blended with the skin and the hair which had been set by the family. The woman recalls that the family had prepared the body 'with love'. In her recollection of this experience, the woman did not discuss a corpse, but rather a body charged with intimate and social meaning. Here, in the woman's account, is a tribute to a person whose presence in the world had none of the autonomy we so greatly value in western society. In this sense, her corpse represented a life that may have been both liberated and enslaved by its connection to others. In life, these connections had included a family (note references to other family members) a home (references to the bed in relation to the rest of room) and a social network (note also references to the community, ie. school). This connection appears to have been so powerful that it maintained a relational power, even in death. The young man senses the loneliness and isolation of the corpse, despite his recognition of the significance of his grandmother's connection to the family in life. How do we account for such differences?

No doubt there are multiple factors that could account for such differences. The events leading up to the death, for example, may have been influential. The grandmother of the young man lived at home, fairly independently prior to suffering a stroke. She had then been rushed into hospital where she died a week or so later. So the young man was not involved in any aspect of the nursing care of his grandmother. He did not witness the death and he did not see her again until, on the day of the funeral, her body was brought to the house in a coffin. There was no period of time for the man to become accustomed to the knowledge that his grandmother was dying. Because of this, his experience of viewing her may have had a sense of the unreal about it. The grandmother of the older woman, however, had suffered a long and chronic illness prior to her death. She had been nursed at home by members of the family, all of whom (including the respondent) knew that she would eventually die. So, unlike the male respondent, the older woman had had time to prepare for her grandmother's death:

> *"And I was staying at my aunt X at the time and she met me outside school, and she said, 'Your grandma is dead; your grandfather wants to see you'."*

The woman does not report any feelings of shock or surprise. From the account she appears to have been resigned to the death.

Another possible reason for the difference in the two accounts is the situation. The younger man viewed his grandmother in a house crowded with other mourners. Although in one sense having a lot of other people there might have been comforting, it did not allow for a situation in which a child could be given any individual attention. In the case of the woman, however, there was only the grandfather present at the house when she went to view her grandmother; and he did have time to prepare her. He did this (it seems from the account) in a very skilled and sensitive way. Indeed, this support begins before she even enters her grandfather's house. The woman recalled that she had been met after school by a relative who tells her of her grandmother's death and prepares her for viewing the body. Although the woman reported some apprehension at the prospect, she was not so afraid that she ignored the request to visit her grandparents' house. Once there, she is met by her grandfather, who, rather than rush the child to view the body, quietly questions and, where appropriate, challenges her fears:

"And my granddad said, 'There is nothing to be afraid of.'"

In this way the grandfather reassures the child, while at the same time gently encouraging her to question the logic underpinning her fears, "He said, was you afraid of your grandmother when she was alive?', and I said 'No.'"

The grandfather continued to question his grand-daughter in this way until he felt confident that she was comfortable about viewing the body. Only then did the grandfather accompany his granddaughter to the bedside. Drawing back the sheet, he said nothing, but he remains by his granddaughter's side, ready to give emotional support and/or explanations if required. Her grandfather's behaviour appears to express what Miles (1990) has referred to as a 'silent presence.' Miles defines silent presence as 'personal use of the self, offering an apparently waiting ear and receptive posture so that people may (if they wish) speak'.

Some readers may feel that the grandfather was wrong to encourage his granddaughter to pay her last respects, particularly since she had expressed a wish not to do so. It is important to consider that the woman's positive recollection of her first encounter with death is by no means universal. Data collected by Roberts (1989) confirms that some children have bitterly resented their parents, and/or other adults for insisting that they pay their last respects to a dead person. None of those interviewed for this study reported such negative experiences. However, several issues need to be considered when forming opinions about scenarios, such as the one discussed above. First, the woman's memory is based on a time (about the mid forties) when mortality rates were quite high in Bolton (Kenny *et al*, 1998a). In addition, we have discussed in this chapter that it was, at this time, sometimes necessary for young people, and even children, to help out with the practicalities of death. Taking these factors into account it may have been the case that the grandfather in the case discussed considered it important that his granddaughter be given an opportunity to confront death for the first time in this supportive way. It seems clear from the account that, from the woman's perspective at least, she was adequately supported. She recalls viewing her grandmother's body, not with fear or revulsion, but rather with 'amazement at the beauty of her.'

The woman concludes her account of the incident by stating that from then on, she was never afraid of a dead body. This child's first encounter with death was quite positive. But it 'worked' and can only be completely understood if related to the social and historical context in which it occurred. This does not mean that, although times have changed, we can learn nothing from such recollections. Rather it suggests that we need to take them apart and examine them more closely in order to 'pull out' the practices reported which can be related to theory, placed into new contexts, and used equally effectively.

At the same time we need to be alert to the danger of making generalisations. The writer Wells (1990) reminds us that, although children do vary according to age in their ability to understand the concept and reality of death, the response of individual children is varied and unpredictable.

'A ten-year-old can act with heartrending adult understanding, while a seventeen-year-old can revert to childhood and seek dependence on a grown up.'

(Wells, 1990)

With regard to the child's motivation for viewing a corpse, the writer did not explore this question. However, in her research, Roberts (*op cit*) found that the respondents' reported reactions to paying their last respects were just as diverse as their motives for doing so. Some respondents remembered being very frightened, but were, nevertheless, forced to pay their last respects by well-meaning adults. Here again, it is important to acknowledge and be guided by the work of many researchers, such as Wells, who have emphasised the importance of respecting the child's wishes. Wells' notes that, while many health-care practitioners consider that attending a funeral can be very supportive, this is not the case for all bereaved children. So for adults to insist on such a thing against a child's wishes can do more harm than good.

Roberts also reported that some of those she interviewed said that they had found viewing a corpse quite exciting. Was this ghoulish interest an inter-war equivalent of going to a horror film, Roberts asks? Young children often appear to have an almost ghoulish interest in dead bodies, but this appears to be related to their need to understand what death is. Another attraction during the inter-war years, which could motivate children to attend a funeral was the funeral tea. During a funeral, children in the north were once quite welcome to call at the house of the bereaved (even if they had not attended the funeral itself) to collect a piece of funeral cake. This was usually a small sponge cake and it is a practice that appears to have died out. Other respondents interviewed by Roberts told of how impressed they were when, as children, they watched a funeral procession for the first time. Here again is evidence of the community spirit, discussed by Roberts (1989) and Kenny (1998a), which a funeral in the north once promoted and, in some instances, still does. Others, interviewed by Roberts, spoke of how 'grand' and 'impressive' the funeral hearses were, especially the horse-drawn type 'people were dying for a ride in that'.

However, it would be wrong to assume that northern children were always provided with adequate support in the past, or that they were involved in death rituals and so forth at all times. Indeed, sometimes they were quite inadequately supported or even excluded. One example of why this could happen was the war years. Most of the Bolton women interviewed discussed the war years, but very few commented on the support received by children who had lost their father in the war. This question was asked by the author towards the end of her data gathering. It is a flaw in the study that the question was not asked sooner. Those who did respond to the question once it was asked, did not consider that children were generally adequately supported if they lost a parent due to the war.

Chris Kenny: *You know when you were a child, some of your friends lost a parent. Were they supported?*

Storyteller: *No, not really. I mean war was just there; it was just a fact because for many of us we*

> *couldn't remember a time when there wasn't*
> *one, and if a child at school lost their*
> *father....well you couldn't always be sure*
> *because sometimes they'd be missing, you*
> *know, but, well they'd just disappear for a few*
> *days and we would be told that such and such*
> *a body had lost their daddy.*

The war years are interesting in that they provide a challenge to current ideas about how fragile children are, particularly with regard to the information they absorb about death.

Although there is evidence to support the view that the public nature of funerals meant that children were inevitably exposed to death rituals from a very early age, it must be acknowledged that the nature and quality of such experiences were diverse and shaped by many issues. It is misleading to make generalisations or clear cut distinctions between the inclusion of children in death rituals in the 'good old days' versus the contemporary exclusion of children and the automatic assumption that this is always a bad thing. Such simplistic perceptions provide a very limited understanding of the past and can discourage comparisons or more detailed analysis of the data collected. Such perceptions can also be harmful, because the implicit presumption underpinning these beliefs is that all bereaved children, regardless of their individuality and levels of understanding, are 'better' if they confront death 'head on'. This could lead to the hypothesis that, since such exposures are 'natural' and 'beneficial', theory and research have nothing to offer in terms of improving the ways in which bereaved children can be supported.

Finally, it is by no means clear when the practices relating to death and funerals discussed in this chapter died out, or indeed, if they have in some areas of Bolton. So, when we talk about the 'good old days', we must identify the time in history to which we are referring.

Chapter 2

Children's understanding of death, dying and bereavement: how this relates to their social and intellectual development

This chapter begins with the story of a six-year-old boy. One day his father took him to visit the grave of his late grandmother. The father had brought some plants to arrange around the grave. Taking out his spade he started to dig. Seeing this his son asked 'Are you digging her up dad (the grandmother) to see if she is all right?' From the conversation that followed it appeared that the child believed that the grave marked the spot of a 'granny flat' underground, in which his grandmother lived. The boy's father tried to explain that this was not the case, that dead means dead, and that the cemetery was a burial place for dead people. Despite the efforts of his father to explain, the boy failed to grasp what 'dead' meant. This became obvious when, seeing a statue of an angel on a gravestone, he exclaimed to his father, 'Oh look dad, one's popped up.' The questions the boy asked that day about the dead and his responses to some of the answers he received reflect the difficulties a child of six years has in grasping the meaning of death. His behaviour reflected his level of intellectual functioning at six years of age. The child's behaviour and observations supported the findings of a psychologist called Jean Piaget, who has carried out substantial research into children's intellectual development.

Individuals usually have a preference for using a particular theory and will often refer to theorists whose work supports and makes sense of their own personal experiences. Because of its personal relevance, such work can often be more effective in helping us to improve our practice. One of the authors has found the work of the child developmental psychologist Piaget useful to her as a mother and as an applied psychologist. She recalls reading his work as a mature student and wishing that she had known about it when her four children were small. Would such knowledge have made her a better mother? This depends on the individual's use of the word 'better'. In the sense that her understanding and tolerance of her children's behaviour at various stages of their development would have been improved, then she could say 'yes, I probably would have been a better mother'. The author also considers that more satisfaction would have been gained from parenting because the behaviour she observed in her children may have been more interesting and meaningful than it appeared at the time. As a mother reading Piaget, she felt that she was reading the truth, so similar were his observations to those she had seen in her own children. Piaget was an applied theorist and his theories have had quite a profound impact on the practice of those who care for young children. These include thanatologists.

Because of its multidisciplinary approach, thanatology has informed our understanding of death, dying and bereavement in diverse ways. This includes an increase in the understanding of children's responses to loss. This chapter focusing mainly on children's intellectual development, draws on the work of those who have used Piaget's theories as a basis for their research into children's understanding of death and bereavement. This is because, as many workers have shown, children's intellectual development parallels their increasing awareness of death.

Piaget based his theory of intellectual development on observations of his own children and those he came into contact with during the course of his work in education. Piaget noticed that children's thinking at different stages of development appears to have specific characteristics that are reflected in the things children say, the questions they ask and the mistakes they make. He followed up his early observations using clinical experiments with children. On the basis of his research, he concluded that children's understanding of the world at different ages, reflected differences in intellectual functioning that were qualitative rather than quantitative. What is important is not how much a child knows at a given age, but rather the nature of his/her understanding (Bee, 1985).

Paiget's work is not without criticisms and limitations. Others have shown that children are far more capable intellectually at various ages than Piaget suggests. They have criticised stage theories generally, on the basis that a person can exhibit characteristics that fit several stages at the same time. It has been argued that, in presenting his stages of intellectual development as a system genetically programmed into the child, Piaget has neglected the influence of the environment. However, the basis of this criticism is fallacious. Piaget was quite clear about the importance of the environment as a means of facilitating the development of the various stages he described (Kastenbaum, 1986).

Despite our acknowledgement of the criticisms outlined above, this chapter is not intended to be an academic discussion of Piaget's work. Rather the aim of the discussion is twofold. Firstly, to draw on Piaget's work to show how others have used his ideas in order to understand and better support a bereaved child. Such understanding may prevent an adult who cares for a bereaved child from misinterpreting his/her loss behaviour, ie. attributing it to awkwardness or stubbornness. Even worse, the carer may presume the child does not need the support that is given to adults in similar situations, assuming instead, 'he/she will get over it in his/her own way.'

The second aim is based on the assumtion that, if people have some understanding of how a child's intellectual development can influence his/her understanding of death, this can then be used as a theoretical basis to help carers improve their care and support of the bereaved child. It is hoped that this theoretical framework will increase the knowledge that readers gain from the following chapters. It may also give the innovations in practice discussed in our concluding chapter greater meaning. Should this happen, such innovations may be replicated by other workers and developed even further.

The authors would also like to point out that, although intellect may play an important role in the ways in which people of any age experience death, so too does the cultural and social context in which such a loss occurs, the personality of the child and the emotional and situational aspects of the experience. Many of these issues will be discussed in relation to the interview data collected and reported in later chapters. The influence of emotion is very difficult to separate from intellect. In very young children, the investigations of people, such as Bowlby who has explored children's emotional development, has been given equal weight to Piaget's work. Indeed, throughout our discussion we have tried to acknowledge the ways in which emotion can shape perception and thus intellectual understanding. We also refer to the work of Kubler-Ross, an American thanatologist who has observed an intuitive or spiritual way of knowing in children.

From his research, Piaget identified four levels of intellectual development in children, each varying according to the child's age. He called these stages; the sensory motor stage (birth to two years), the pre-operational stage (two to six years), the concrete operational stage (six to twelve years) and the formal operational stage (twelve years onwards). There are individual variations in the way that children progress from one stage to the next and there is a considerable overlap in the level of the intellectual abilities that can be expected from each child. In order to pass from one stage to the next, the child needs to interact with the environment and he or she needs to be exposed to intellectual challenge and stimulation.

Section 1: The sensory motor stage: birth to two years of age

During the first stage of development, the sensory motor stage, the child understands the world in terms of the sensations he or she derives from interactions with objects or people in the world. The child is unable to understand that objects or people can continue to exist even when they are out of sight. For children of this age, out of sight means out of mind. Psychologists call this inability to understand the way things exist, even when out of sight, 'object permanence'. The psychologist, John Bowlby (1969), stressed the importance of the presence of the mother during the early years of a child's life. His theories caused some working mothers to experience unnecessary feelings of guilt because they had to leave their children with an alternative care giver while they went out to work. His work also led many to conclude that the loss of the mother at an early age, for whatever reason, could cause irreversible long-term psychological damage to the child.

Bowlby's work has been criticised in recent years by other workers who have found that it is not so much separation from the mother that can be harmful, but rather the circumstances in which this occurs. They have also noted the importance of the quality of alternative support available in a mother's absence. Clark and Clark (1976) have also produced evidence to suggest that children, even after suffering the most extreme deprivation and lack of love and care, can be rehabilitated at a later stage of development than that anticipated by Bowlby, if support and love is provided. In response to the work of his critics, Bowlby has modified much of his early work.

Care of a young baby's physical needs is, without doubt, important but, despite the criticisms of his work, Bowlby has been instrumental in drawing attention to the additional importance of emotional love and support. He has also alerted researchers to the profound distress a young child experiences if separated from someone he/she cares about. His work was to have a direct impact on policy and practices. Soon, other workers, such as the Robertsons (cited in Bee, 1985), began to explore separation of the child from his/her parents, ie. in hospitals. It is largely due to the work of the Robertsons that we now have such open visiting in hospitals with accommodation provided so that parents can stay as residents. Up to the age of two years, children have no conceptual understanding of death. Nevertheless, their response to separation is intense and fearful. Young babies make their distress clear by crying (Dyregrow and Kingsley, 1991). Older babies and toddlers may appear quite unconcerned, but this can be deceiving. Bowlby and his co-worker, Mary Ainsworth, (Bee, 1985) described this behaviour as 'detachment'.

A child who is described as detached may appear to have recovered from a separation when, in fact, he/she has repressed the painful memories of the separation. However, painful experiences hidden in the unconscious in this way, can be quite damaging. Klein (1960) argued that in severe cases this can lead to a condition she referred to as 'splitting'. According to her analysis, every time the child experiences frustration due to separation, she/he experiences anger towards the 'bad' ungiving mother. But the child needs to love the good mother on whom he or she depends. Young children cannot comprehend both good and bad in the same person, so they split the mother into two persona. The good mother is the one who provides and she remains in the conscious mind. At the same time, the bad mother who fails to provide, is pushed to the unconscious.

On one level this may seem an effective way of coping with uncomfortable feelings. However, Klein considers that each time the conscious mind assigns part of its experience to the unconscious, it dilutes itself. If this happens too often for an individual child to cope with, the conscious mind, or ego becomes depleted. The sense of fragmentation caused by this can lead to personality and/or mental health problems later in life. Douglas (1989) and Brown and Harris (1978) have shown that young children who experience a bereavement are vulnerable to periods of depression in later life.

Although a child described as detached can be deceiving, a perceptive adult will often see that such young children express symptoms of grieving, ie. pining. They may also call out or search for the absent care giver (Parkes, 1970). Despite the terrible distress experienced by a child suffering from separation, his/her relationship with care givers is one of dependency and a concern by the child that his/her emotional and physical needs are met. This is not to dismiss the above discussion, but rather to point out that, as children grow older, their relationships become much more complex and can be based on other needs, such as intellectual interests, friendship and companionship.

The work of psychologists, such as Piaget (1952) and Bruner (cited by Bee, 1985), suggests that, during the early years of life, children do not have the intellectual ability to build up detailed memories. It is unlikely that children who are bereaved when very young will have detailed memories of the person they have lost. If a suitable carer is found the child may not necessarily suffer extreme emotional long-term ill effects. Sometimes the child, as he/she grows older, may develop an idealistic image of the lost parent. In terms of support and relationships, this can be very important because such children may believe that no one can live up to this 'perfect' parent (Lendrum and Syme, 1992).

Between the ages of eighteen months and two years, the child begins to develop language. This helps children by providing a tool with which they can name their feelings and explain what is troubling them. Because a young child's language skills are relatively basic, a busy or inexperienced care giver can misinterpret what the child is trying to say, or may underestimate the intensity of the feelings that the child is experiencing. Lendrum and Syme note that a child of about two years of age may say that he/she is 'very, very, very sad' using repetition of the word 'very' several times, rather like the rhythm of a nursery rhyme. This may result in adults not taking what the child says seriously. Yet the connection between the rhythmic nature of the nursery rhyme and the young child's fascination with it, is related to his/her emotional experience and perceptions (Higgins, 1993). Adults can also misunderstand words that the child uses inappropriately (at least, from an adult point of view). For example, young children will frequently use the word 'bored' to describe feelings of deep isolation, grief and loneliness (Lendrum and Syme, *op cit*). If the adults responsible for the care of the child are unaware of this tendency, they may respond inappropriately, for example, finding the child something to do. When the child swiftly loses interest, care givers may become frustrated. An understanding of this behaviour may reduce such feelings of frustration.

Section 2: The pre-operational stage: two to six years of age

Piaget has been criticised for his description of the pre-operational stage of development. This may be because he focused his observations more on what the child could not do rather than on what he/she was capable of doing. Others, who have followed up his work, have shown that, during this stage of development, children are far more capable than Piaget considered them to be. However, some of the intellectual abilities and perspectives he identified, are quite important when considering how children understand death. At the pre-, and indeed, concrete operational stage, the child understands the world in terms of direct experience and practicalities.

This observation corresponds with the work of Fitzgerald (1992), who found that children between the ages of two and five years of age cannot conceptualise death. Because of this they assume that dead people live in another dimension (recall the opening paragraph). Typically, at this age, the child is interested in how the dead person manages the activities of daily living. By the time the child has reached the age of six years, he or she understands that death is irreversible and that whatever death is, it is not the same as being a different kind of alive. None of the young people interviewed could remember exactly how old they were when they became completely aware of death. Most placed this awareness at around the ages of six or seven years and it was often a sudden awareness caused by the death of someone they knew, usually a grandparent. However, they could all remember a time when they were unaware of death as a stage of simply not knowing:

"I never used to think about it at all to be honest, until my granddad died, and then I understood it a bit. My mum explained it to me but to be honest it took me a long time to understand. You just don't think about it really, I mean, when you are a kid well you have all that future ahead of you, time seems like forever. Like when you are at school I can remember being at school and thinking that it would last forever. I knew that it wouldn't, I had this vague idea of what I might be doing when I grew up. But it wasn't something I could sort of, see as real because, well I just thought that I would go on for ever just like time, because that goes on forever."

The concept of time can add to the difficulties a child has in understanding death, because children have no conception of time outside 'now' — as any adult who has tried to explain tomorrow or yesterday to a young child will tell you. Time, as a young child experiences it in most societies, is organised around cycles or routines in which everything is repeated. It seems logical within such a conceptual framework to assume that we start off little, grow big, die and then come back as little again (Dyregrow and Kingsley, 1991). The routine of life was acknowledged by one of the young men interviewed and he remembered how this interfered with his ability to understand the concept of death.

"I mean, as you get older, you get used to the fact that as one thing ends another begins. You know, things continue, one thing follows another. So once you get used to that it's really difficult to imagine something just ending, especially, you. I sometimes think that's the way people have faith really, it's a way of coping, coping with the end of me, if you see what I mean. It's a hope that you will go on. I think that nothing ends. But sometimes I wonder, am I just telling myself that to cope."

Towards the ages of six or seven years, awareness begins to develop. However, the child may still be struggling to understand and may prefer to deny the reality of his/her own mortality. At this age children want to know why people die, how they die and what happens when they die. One way in which children appear to work towards an understanding of death is reflected through play, for example, when they 'play dead.' Anthony (1971) has argued that, just as interesting as children's understanding of death, is their understanding of what is living. She found that very young children attribute qualities of life to almost anything that moves. Thus from the child's point of view, the sun and the moon are assumed to be living things, as are many other inanimate objects. Little wonder that, at this stage of development, children have difficulty in understanding death.

Rochlin (1967) found that, by the time children reach the ages of three to four years, they are able to understand that death represents the end of vital functions. For example, dead people cannot breathe, their heart does not beat and so forth. This is understanding 'death' at its earliest stage and children are eager to explore the new 'discovery'. At this age, children may bring home dead animals and birds. However, because the child has still not grasped that dead means dead forever, he/she may still make attempts to restore life. Issacs (1930) found that, at this age, children will attempt to revive a dead animal by putting it in water. Anthony (*op cit*) comments that such misunderstandings may arise because the child has seen adults putting flowers in water to revive them. There are times when attempts at revival can be successful, as the following extract from the transcript of a Bolton woman in her thirties shows:

"I remember being very young when I started noticing when people talked about death, I'm not sure how old I was but I do remember that I was at primary school. Anyway, I didn't believe it. I just did not believe that people would die. 'This creature is living and breathing' I would think to myself, 'and it just cannot stop.' Anyway, one day my sister and me, we were playing out and we found this hedgehog. My sister said that it was dead so she put it in a shoe box and buried it and gave it a nice, proper funeral, prayers, service, stick headstone, the lot. But I didn't believe that it was dead, this hedgehog, so I waited until she had gone and I dug it up. And I poked it and poked it until (laughs) *it came to life. You know, the poor thing must have been hibernating, or asleep, but anyway, it came to life. So that made it even worse for me to accept death because I had already 'revived' one dead thing, so I could not really see why people could not revive other dead things."*

There are several potential difficulties that can arise at this stage, which can complicate the child's acceptance of death. This is may be due to the tendency for children at this age to engage in fantasy play, to the child's interest in cause and effect, or to both. Anthony notes that, in cause/effect relationships, young children of about three to four years of age will often refer to a dead person as 'killed' or 'murdered'. This indicates an assumption that 'dead' is something that is done to someone. Although feelings of guilt are typical at any age after a bereavement, children at the pre-operational stage are at greater risk of assuming that they may have caused the death of someone they love. This thought process is referred to by Piaget as transductive thinking. Bee (1985) describes it as a disposition to think that, because two things happen together, one caused the other. To illustrate this, Bee uses an example given by Piaget of his daughter Lucienne, who announced one afternoon her disbelief that it was the afternoon because she had not had her nap. In other words, Lucienne believed that the nap had caused the afternoon to happen. Several writers have pointed out that something a deceased parent may have said to a child prior to death, such as 'you'll be the death of me' or something the child may have said to the parent, eg. 'I hate you, I wish you were dead', can cause the child to believe that she/he has 'killed' the dead parent.

The role of fantasy is also very important because, as Kitzinger and Kitzinger (1989) argue, the child's ability to fantasise can:

(a)   make it difficult for the child to distinguish between fact and fantasy, so that guilty thoughts such as those discussed above can become real to the child.

(b)   if parents and other adults are not honest or clear in what they tell the child, then he/she will develop his/her own theories.

Fantasy is quite important in shaping the perceptual world of the child. During the pre-operational stage, the child becomes increasingly aware of death, but finds it difficult to articulate or define this awareness. This early understanding of death is manifest in children's preoccupations and fears about something 'out there' which is waiting to get them. In order to avoid this 'something', children avoid stepping on the lines on the pavement, in case the devil gets them. Before they go to sleep, they check in the wardrobe or under the bed to make sure that the 'something' is not waiting to 'pounce' once they go to sleep. The 'something' is usually personified in the shape of the devil or the bogey man (Gordon, 1986). Once again, adults have to be very careful how they describe death to children of this age. If they say it is similar to 'going to sleep' then children may be afraid to go to sleep in case they do not wake up again (Kitzinger and Kitzinger, 1989; Lendrum and Syme, 1992; Smith and Pennells, 1995).

Generally, the child's tendency to fantasise can lead to some amusing theories about what happens to people once they die. Stanley Hall *et al* (1921) found that some children, who have been told that the dead go to a heaven that is in the sky, believe that the dead climb there on something like a ladder or rope. Another child, having been told by his mother that they must drink the cream before it goes bad (the rationale given to the child that all things that have been living go bad once dead) asked if God bought children from shops in heaven to eat. Children can also have problems if adults explain to them that people have to die to make room for the living. Kitzinger and Kitzinger discuss the case of a little boy who, having been told this by his parents, bitterly resented his little sister, who was born a few weeks after the death of his grandfather. This was because he believed that her birth had caused the former's death.

One of the young people interviewed (aged 19 years) remembers with some amusement his ideas about death when he was six years old:

"When you are a kid you think about heaven and all that, you don't think about people being dead. Well I didn't, not in the way that I think about it now. Anyway, I thought about death in terms of good and bad, the good went to heaven and the bad went to hell ... I used to think about heaven a lot. I used to look out at the clouds at night and think 'I wonder if I'll see someone running across' (laughs). *I mean, heaven was like, up in the clouds, and hell was down there* (pointing down) *stuck underground and horrible. Horrible in the sense that, I mean I can't say that it frightened me in the way you hear about some kids being scared, it was more like being sent to bed early. You know, I mean, if you're in heaven you have the freedom to hop around on the clouds but if you were in hell then that meant a sad time. It meant being stuck in when you can't go out anywhere. It was boring and like I say ... like being sent to bed early."*

Another young man aged 20 years when interviewed recalled that:

"Heaven was definitely up in the sky. That's what the clouds were for, they were like little islands that the dead stood about on. I remember seeing those cartoons with little angels on and that's exactly how I thought of heaven. I even used to wonder, when I saw a plane, why some of the dead didn't get knocked off from time to time. And I certainly couldn't understand why none of my friends who had been on holiday on a plane never reported seeing any (dead people). In fact, I can remember actually hoping that some friends of my mum and dad

who'd been away might mention seeing one. Eventually, I just came to the conclusion that the dead must be invisible, I mean, how else could you explain that no one who had been on a plane had ever seen one."

The theme of childhood recollections of what heaven and hell would be like was shared by all members of the group interviewed:

"Yes, that's how I saw heaven and hell. I thought that when you died you definitely went to either heaven or hell. Heaven was peaceful and behind the clouds, you know? I saw the clouds as like a barrier that divided earth and heaven, and in heaven you met up with all the people you knew who had died. I was quite definite in my head about that. Heaven was in the clouds and hell was in the centre of the earth. And it's amazing really how as a kid you can pick up on little things you see or hear. I remember once seeing on telly this volcano, and I thought that was like a hole in the earth leading to hell (laughs). *I even remember watching it with great interest and you know when all that hot lava comes out. I remember thinking to myself, quite sensibly, 'yes, well that's what you'd expect, I suppose the fire can get a bit too big and sort of, overflow like that sometimes.'"*

Another adult man in his 30s remembers his complete refusal as a child to believe that he ever would die:

" I just thought, I don't believe it, I don't have to think about it because by the time I get to that age they'll have developed a cure for it. Really, I did. And when they had that first heart transplant, well that just confirmed it for me. I thought, right, I've cracked it now, all they need to do is think up a brain transplant and I'm OK."

Even after the death of his grandfather (which for all of the young people interviewed was the first significant event in their lives to bring the reality of death home) the man remembered telling himself that dead people get a second chance:

"I mean even after my granddad died I prayed every night for God to make him come back. I used to pray that I'd get up in the morning and that God would make

everything just as it was before he had died. He never did of course and as the weeks went on I started to understand that he was dead and that he would not come back ever. But even then, accepting his death wasn't the same as accepting my own. I just kept on telling myself, 'I'll get away with it, just see, it won't happen to me. I'll be one of those who gets away with it.'"

This extract reinforces the difficulty that people of any age have in accepting their own mortality. Some never do, of course, as shown by the following quote from a woman who was in her late 30s at the time of her interview:

"Do I ever think about my own death. I'm not going to die . . . I hope."

For others, their amazement that anyone would be interested in such questions gave some indication of their reluctance to think about the subject. Yet this is something about which they clearly felt ambivalent. Although the young adult man, quoted below, responded to the question 'do you ever think about your own death' in the following way:

"What kind of a question is that! I'm absolutely dumbfounded. How astonishing . . . (laughter). I am truly amazed that you would ask me that question."

He still went on to participate in the interview, became, after his initial amazement, interested in the discussions and provided some excellent data on his feelings about life and death. Whether or not children at the pre- and concrete operational stages of development have difficulties in understanding the concept of death, the interviews with the adults who took part in the study suggest that people never really come to terms with the prospect. It is our inability to accept the reality of our own mortality that makes us so ambivalent about it. Dyregrow and Kingsley (1991) note that, as children develop 'death awareness', they also appear to develop a morbid fascination with death, this being just one of the ways in which they come to accept its inevitability. This morbid fascination with death appears to be something we carry with us for most of our lives. Thus, at one level we want to discuss death, think about it and maintain our morbid fascination, while on another, we ignore our mortality, believing unconsciously that we will be one of the ones to 'get away with it.'

The discussion has tried to illustrate the creativity of the child and the way this contributes to the ability to use the information available so that he/she can draw his/her own conclusions. Some of the conclusions which children reach on the basis of such information may be quite incorrect and a source of worry, interest and even amusement to adults. But the tendency for children to make connections between the different things they observe, is really no different from the way in which adults, including scientists, make sense of their world. Therefore, if children have misunderstandings about death, this may reflect the way in which those who care for the child have conveyed the information. Often, when such misunderstandings arise, adults have only themselves to blame.

Section 3: The concrete operational stage: six to twelve years of age

By the time children reach the concrete operational stage, they have made quite a leap forward in terms of their intellectual development (Bee, *op cit*). They can understand and perform mental tasks, such as subtraction, abstraction and class inclusion (in other words, they can group things into categories). Despite these developments, children are still limited to understanding in concrete terms. For children to understand something, they need to be given examples drawn from their own experiences to illustrate the point. Even at this stage of development, children have difficulty understanding that death is irreversible, and they may be very concerned to find out how a dead person manages (Kastenbaum, 1967).

By seven years of age, the child begins to grasp that death is irreversible, but still finds difficulty in imagining his/her own death sometime in the future. This is also true of many adults. The interviewee cited below (aged 36 years at the time of the interview) responded to the question, 'Can you remember at what age you realised that you will die one day?' with the following:

"I never did . . . seriously. Not really, I don't think I realise it even now. I mean, I know there is a fact that I will die someday. But I don't think I will die one day, if you see what I mean? Sometimes, now that I'm starting to get older and I've experienced some ill health, not a lot, but you know? I'm not as quick or as healthy as I used to be, well then I can believe it, well I can think about it, put it that way. But really, otherwise, most of the time I just cannot comprehend it. I just cannot comprehend the fact that one day I will go, I will die and that will be for good. I think that's why I believe in reincarnation. I just cannot believe that my life will end, so I think we get another chance. I believe that we get lots and lots and lots of chances, living lots of lives, living as lots of different people, living in lots of different bodies."

The idea that reincarnation offers another chance was put forward by some of the younger people who were interviewed. This theme is discussed later in the section on adolescence. For the moment, however, it is worth noting when considering the extract of the transcript cited above, that although many of the themes discussed in this chapter relate to children's perceptions of death, how many of us ever come to terms completely with our own mortality. While children's thoughts differ from adults in some ways, their thoughts about death are similar. By the time the child has reached the concrete operational stage, it seems that there are more similarities than differences between adults and children. Young children may need concrete examples, such as pictures, tombstones and rituals in order to reinforce the reality of the loss, but so do many adults. Indeed, one of the advantages of funerals is that they help to reinforce the reality of a loss (Worden, 1991).

Slowly the child begins to realise that one day he/she will die, in other words the child begins to recognise his or her mortality. This knowledge can be quite disturbing. For example, Gorer (1965) recalls crying himself to sleep every night for weeks when, as a child, he began to recognise his own mortality. Sometimes, the child's awareness of mortality can be traumatic, and even frightening, despite the support of parents or caregivers. One of the young people interviewed, recalls his worries about death when he was about seven years of age.

"When my grandma died I realised that one day I would die and that one day I would end up in a box like her in the ground — I shit myself. My brother and I cried ourselves to sleep every night. When my grandma died, my parents were honest and supportive, I have to give them that. But it was something that only I could work out for myself, it was a very personal thing, and in a way I felt angry with my parents. There was nothing rational about it, it was really weird because I couldn't tell them how angry I was with them because I knew that it was unreasonable. But how, can I put it, I felt very let down by them. You see, what it was, before then I was a kid and everything was secure and everything was done for me and I thought that my parents could do anything for me. I believed that I could depend on them completely. But once I started to understand about death, I realised that one day, I would grow old and wrinkly and then I would die. And that was the one thing that my parents could not do for me — they couldn't stop me from dying."

Phenomenology is a field of psychology that explores the complete loneliness in which human beings live out their existence. This 'existential loneliness' is the realisation that, since our individual experience is just that, totally individual, no one else can experience it with us. It would appear from the extract above that death awareness in the child parallels his or her increasing awareness of this separateness, this 'aloneness.' When we consider the discussion earlier of the distress children feel at separation from a care giver, it is little wonder that awareness of the inevitable separateness of all human existence can be quite daunting to a child. And if there is one experience in which we are quite alone, it is in death. Writing of her mother's death, Simon De Beauvoir (1964) remembers the funeral:

'Is she there?' asked my sister. 'Yes.' She gave a short sob: 'The only comfort I have,' she said 'is that it will happen to me too. Otherwise it would be too unfair.' Yes. We were taking part in a dress rehearsal for our own funeral. The

misfortune is that although everyone must come to this, each experiences the journey in solitude.

However, the child gradually begins to understand that there are some bonuses to this, a point also made by De Beauvoir (1959):

One day in the Place Saint-Ulpice, walking along hand in hand with my Aunt Marguerite who hadn't the remotest idea how to talk to me, I suddenly wondered 'How does she see me?' and felt a sharp sense of superiority for I knew what I was like inside, she didn't. Deceived by outward appearances, she never suspected that inside my immature body nothing was lacking and I made up my mind that when I was older I would never forget that a five-year-old is a complete individual, a character in his own right.

For one of the young men interviewed, it was the fear of growing old that presented the greater dread. Although, from what he said about ageing, fear of loneliness and isolation were his main worries, not ageing in itself.

"I think I was about eight, seven or eight when I realised that I would die. I used to be scared of it when I was little, mainly because I thought that dying must be painful, and it was the fear of nothing. I can't explain it, you know, the fear that when you are dead there is nothing. As I got older, I just accepted that I would die one day. But what started to worry me more was the fear of growing old. I don't want to die young or anything like that, you know, I'd like to live a bit, have some kids and watch them grow and all that. But when I get to the age when my legs start to give and I start to find it hard to get out and get about. And another thing is that, I wouldn't like to be one of these old people who live the longest, you know, you get these who live to a ripe old age so to speak. But everyone they went to school with and grew up with has died. I'd really hate that, because when you think about it, the world is changing all the time. But it's exciting, change when you can share it with your friends. But imagine what it must be like for all these really old people ... you know, everyone they knew have died. They can't get out

because their legs have given in, and the only people they get to meet are those who . . . if this makes sense, you know, people who come to look after them. People who come from, I suppose, a different world I'd really hate that."

Fear of the experience of dying was shared by two other young people in the group, as one put it:

"That's why I'd like to die in my sleep, or be unconscious. What really frightens me is knowing that you are going to die, actually feeling death coming on. And to be completely conscious and helpless to stop it."

Having seen the film 'Dead Man Walking' a few months prior to the interview, one of the young men interviewed added:

'Yes, that to me is the terrible thing about capital punishment, that you would know the actual, precise moment. I used to think that there could be kinder ways of killing people, but even with that lethal injection, you know, the idea is that if they put you to sleep you won't know when you die. But that's rubbish really! You know when they make you unconscious that you'll never wake up again, and that's the difference! When you die in your sleep naturally, you do not know that you will never wake up again. So you go to sleep and there is hope, you know, hope for another day . . . that's not the same thing with lethal injection."

Once children become aware of death, they develop an interest in death rituals, especially funerals. Dyregrow and Kingsley (1991) write that there is no evidence to suggest that it is harmful for children to attend funerals if this is what they wish to do. Indeed, as data collected by Weller *et al* (1988) suggests, the reverse appears to be true, in that many adults recall as children, bitterly resenting being excluded from the funerals of people they loved. However, research also suggests that children should not be made to participate in death rituals (Weller *et al*, 1988), and that if they do attend a funeral they should be supported (McCown, 1984). Providers of such support can vary and this will be discussed in the concluding chapter. The child needs to be informed of what to expect and it is important that he/she is given a choice (McCown, *op cit*).

Although children during both the pre- and concrete operational stages of development find it difficult to understand anything outside their own experience, once something becomes part of their reality they wish to explore it. Death is no different from anything else in this respect, children need to make it 'real'. Dyregrow and Kingsley (*op cit*) caution that this can lead to children behaving in ways which adults, if they fail to understand or are overcome by grief, may find quite distressing.

Dyregrow and Kingsley write that it is not uncommon for children to want to touch a corpse and to examine it by, for example, trying to open the mouth or eyes. Dyregrow and Kingsley argue that these are other ways in which children try to make death seem real. The writers also point out that such curiosity is quite typical in all children, many of whom may try to examine an adult's face when the latter is sleeping. Some writers have noted that a bereaved child may occasionally become preoccupied with memories of the deceased, and may wish to repeat certain experiences over and over again. Behaviour in these situations may include looking at pictures of the deceased, asking to be told stories about the deceased, reading, or asking adults to read, letters from the deceased, sometimes repeatedly. In order to feel close, the child may carry around an object that had once belonged to the person who has died and even hide it to keep it safe. The child may wish to touch and smell items of clothing or sit in the deceased's chair. Such behaviour suggests that the child is trying to get close to the dead person.

A bereaved child's limited ability to distinguish fact from fantasy may cause him/her to imagine that she/he has been visited by the deceased (Dyregrow and Kingley, 1991; Lendrum and Syme, 1992). Kubler-Ross (1983) considers that such fantasies can be quite comforting to a bereaved child. She recommends preparing children for such an experience by telling them that the deceased may come to visit them in their dreams. Kubler-Ross is, however, quite a religious person and her advice on matters such as this might not be considered appropriate by parents who do not share her religious beliefs. Lendrum and Syme (*op cit*) also note that a bereaved child can sometimes over-identify and adopt some behaviours and mannerisms linked with the deceased. Again such behaviour can be observed in bereaved adults. Simon De Beauvior, in her autobiographic account of the weeks leading up to her mother's death, writes of how she would occasionally talk and act like her mother. Although such behaviour can be quite distressing to adults, the writers cited in this section insist that children do work through them with support.

In conclusion, *Sections 1, 2* and *3* of this chapter have explored younger children's perceptions, responses to and understanding of death, dying and bereavement from the point of view of their intellectual development. Adolescence will be dealt with in Section 5 and is related to research that has explored the meaning which young people attach to life and death. The following section discusses a form of understanding in young children, described by the thanatologist Elizabeth Kubler-Ross. This alternative way of knowing she describes as intuitive or spiritual knowing.

Section 4: Intuitive or spiritual knowing in children

The work of psychologists such as Piaget and Bowlby (and those influenced by them) has been useful in helping us to understand children's intellectual and emotional understanding of death. Kubler-Ross has identified another form of understanding in dying children that she refers to as intuitive or spiritual knowing. On this level, Kubler-Ross argues that children have a deeper awareness of death than some adults give them credit for. In her work with dying children, she has found they often know that they are going to die, not at a conscious or intellectual level but at a spiritual level. Such children will often ask their parents if they are dying. She writes that if parents and other adults fail to be truthful with the child then he/she will share his/her concerns with other children. She acknowledges that young children in particular have difficulty in explaining to adults what their worries are. She also describes a form of communication which she calls symbolic language.

Children use this symbolic language to voice their concerns with other children. These are often the concerns children feel unable to share with adults. Kubler-Ross argues that children share many secrets in this way of which adults are unaware. She also argues that in many ways, a dying child has more wisdom than adults and considers that if parents of a dying child fail to be truthful then they miss the opportunity of sharing the child's world. Parents of dying children will eventually lose their child so it seems a tragedy for them to also lose these sharing experiencies. Kubler-Ross believes that painful experiences can lead, in the long-term, to spiritual and emotional growth.

Kubler-Ross stresses the importance of honesty and cautions parents of terminally ill children against hiding their emotions. If the child finds that the parent has been crying then, she recommends that the parent takes the child in his/her arms and explains that he/she is crying because of his/her sadness that the child is dying. Sharing unhappy experiences with a dying child, does not cause guilt or fear. Rather, it makes the child feel loved. One common source of regret in the bereaved, observed by one of the authors, is that they may not have had a chance to tell the deceased how much they loved him/her before he/she died. One of the young women interviewed spoke of the experiences she had shared with her late father:

"Its funny the things that you do remember, I mean, I was very young when my father died. One thing I really remember very clearly was one afternoon when he took me in town. He really spoiled me and then we went in a coffee bar and he bought me a drink and then he gave me a Cadburys' Cream Egg that he'd bought in town. I remember biting into it for the first time, and being really surprised like, the skin was really hard chocolate, and then all this goo ran down my chin. We had a really good laugh about that. Whenever I think about my dad I think about that Cadburys' Cream Egg. And do you know what I regret? I really, really regret that I can't tell him how much it meant to me — I wish I could thank him now for that Cadburys' Cream Egg."

Such feelings of regret are common in the bereaved. It is for this reason that the author's late grandmother stressed the importance of saying a 'proper' goodbye when people part from one another. She always said 'you never know once they walk out of that door, you might never see them again.' What better opportunity could there be, than the one described in the above scene, to tell someone how much you love them, before it is too late? But, in reality, when we experience bereavement, there are always things we wish we had said to the deceased and this can lead to unnecessary feelings of guilt. Unnecessary because we could never say all the things in a lifetime that we would like to say and anyway, it is sometimes only the loss of someone that makes such things relevant anyway. The young woman quoted above probably did thank her father for the egg at the time. It was not the giving of the egg that was important but rather, the quite ordinary experience she describes. This is the type of thing we share with those we love all the time. It is only when the opportunity for such experiences is lost that we realise how precious they were. In reality it is not what she did or did not say that the young woman mourns but rather, the fact that she has lost the potential to ever say it. The significance of the story quoted above is that it makes explicit the fact that, in relationships, it is the little, seemingly insignificant things, the sharing of experiences which matter. The sharing of ordinary experiences and their perceived ordinariness, provides a measure of how securely bound to each other people in relationships can be. The above extract provides one example of how limitations of research can become apparent. Reading the extract quoted gives readers little feeling of how emotionally charged it was. It does not adequately convey the way in which the interviewer witnessed how the young woman tried as she spoke, to relive the moment she described. One of the most notable things about the narrative above, is its sensuality, the way that the speaker tries to conjure up every sight, every sound, every feeling and physical sensation of her memory of the afternoon she shared with her father.

Kubler-Ross believes that siblings and other children who have contact with a dying child should be told the truth and that all connected with him or her should be included in the care and support if they so wish:

"Children of all ages who have been included in the care of a terminally ill child are not shocked and traumatised

> *by the final sight of a cathartic sibling, sometimes with a blown up abdomen and blue marks on hands and arms. They see the sick child with different eyes; they communicate on different levels. Such sights shock only those who have not been part of the daily care of the sick child, but those visitors naturally need to be informed before they enter the sickroom.'*

(Kubler Ross, 1983)

Kubler-Ross also stresses that it is important to avoiding spoiling a terminally ill child. Ironically, with less than honesty, this can be one way parents tell their child that he/she is dying. She argues that to spoil the child is to deny the spontaneity that comes with relationships, including the feelings of anger, frustration and disagreements that are all a part of family and community life. Spoiling a terminal child can also lead to the neglect of other siblings, who may come to resent the dying sister or brother, thus preventing siblings from getting the best out of the relationship. It could even lead to the surviving child suffering feelings of guilt later in life. Kubler-Ross is a very religious woman and this is clear in some of the thoughts she has written about death and dying. However, her work is useful to all involved in the care of the dying, regardless of their religious affiliations.

Readers of her work may not agree with everything she writes. Indeed many of her ideas have been criticised by other thanatologists, particularly those who disagree with her stage theory of dying. However, many readers will find at least some aspects of her work very valuable, mainly because of the humanistic element that she brings to it.

Section 5: Adolescence and death

By the time that young people reach early puberty and adolescence, beginning around the age of twelve years, they have developed to the Formal Operational Stage (Piaget, 1952). They are capable of abstract thinking, ie. they can think of possibilities that are outside their own experience. Hughes (1995) writes that, by this stage of development, young people are aware that once someone has died, that person is dead forever and they are also aware of their own mortality. Between the ages of nine and twelve years, children usually want to be involved in death rituals, such as funerals. Adolescents, however, tend to be outraged by the death of someone they care about. Hughes argues that, at this stage in young people's lives, the peer group has more influence than parents and other older people. This dependence on the peer group can effect young bereaved people in a number of ways, depending on the values and level of understanding within the group.

Some young people may cry and grieve openly with their friends. Others, if the loss sets them apart from the group, may hide or even deny that a death or loss has occurred. This can also happen in loss caused by the divorce of parents. Corr and McNeil (1986) write of young adolescents who develop an interest in mysticism or the occult. Such interests reflect a desire to come to terms with their own mortality and to find some meaning to life. Two of the young people who took part in the focus group interview remembered a phase in their lives when they became fascinated with the paranormal. One young man's interest in the occult had been influenced by tales of the Lancaster Witches:

"I remember hearing about the witches around here. Me and my friends used to go up on the moors around Bolton and Rivington looking for witches caverns and all that. Really up there (the moors) it's quite atmospheric, especially if you've heard all about the witch trials. I even went so far as to have a try on the ouija board, but I didn't keep that up for very long. I think that's very dangerous actually."

Another took a more spiritual approach:

"I did get interested in astral projection for a time. I got really in to it. I went to some meetings and read some books. I tried to do it once, but it didn't work. I do think though, even now that there is some kind of barrier between life and death and that when you die you have to cross that. That's the danger as I see it of that kind of experimentation. Seriously, I think that if you play around with that kind of thing, then there is a danger you

could find yourself stuck in the barrier between two worlds and unable to escape from either. I mean, it's not that daft an idea, lots of cultures believe things like that. And who is to say who is right and who is wrong. There's no ones come back so far as I know to tell us what's right. I can understand why people want to experiment, like I say, I've done it myself. But I think that you are playing with fire."

Adolescence is the age when most young people begin to ask questions about 'What is it all for?' Their attitude to death is mainly governed by their attitude to life. Gordon (1986) writes that early adolescence is characterised by an increasing understanding and awareness of death, while late adolescence is characterised by trying to attach some meaning to life and death. This, Gordon argues, fills the future with hope. A future that promises no hope leads to a death of the spirit and possibly suicide. It was interesting that, during a focus group interview conducted for this study, all the young people in the group expressed a belief in reincarnation. This surprised the author because at their age, she and most of her friends had extremely diverse views about what happened after death. One young man's belief in reincarnation appeared to be associated with comments he had made about fear of isolation and disability in old age:

"I believe in reincarnation. I believe this body (pointing to his chest) *it's got all these organs keeping it going, keeping it ticking over, but there must be more to it than that. You know, there has to be more inside, and that must be the spirit. In a sense the spirit is trapped in the body. More so if you can't walk or get about. So in a sense when you get old, death I think can be quite a good thing. Because then the soul is released, it's free you know, ready to live another life."*

Each of the six young people in the focus group felt that belief in reincarnation was quite a general thing among young people in the nineties.

"I don't think it's just us, most of my friends believe in reincarnation. In fact, as far as I know, they all do. I don't believe in heaven and hell any more. A lot less

people are religious now, which I think is where the idea of heaven and hell comes from. But as well as that, I think that as you get older, I mean, I just can't think that this is it, that this is all my life is about. There has to be something else, but what? Reincarnation seems believable.'

The young people who took part in the focus group interview were asked why they believed in reincarnation. They were also asked, if they believed that spirits had to wait to be reborn, what did they believe happened to these spirits in between death and reincarnation. Only one young man in the group volunteered an answer to the second question.

"Well to be honest, I'd never thought about that an awful lot. I suppose they are all around us the dead. But I'm not so sure that they exist like, as ghosts. They are there but in like, another dimension. But then I'm not sure that they are individual souls as such, more like energy. Yes. You know how energy can change its shape, when I think about it I suppose that's how I see it. Life is an energy, it comes out sometimes as a person, a particular person. Then that person dies, right. Then it comes back in another form, a new person."

The rest of the group agreed with the speaker and considered that this explanation provided a reasonable answer to the question. In answer to the first question, why do you believe in reincarnation? One member of the group, a young man gave an interesting answer:

"I don't know really, but its like, it's important if you believe in reincarnation to live a good life. I believe that if you live a good life this time around you'll live a good life in the future. So living a good life now is a way of storing up good lives for the future. But then even if you don't live such a good life now, if you at least try then you have another chance, yes that's I suppose what reincarnation means to me, another chance."

The writer found this unanimous agreement with the belief in reincarnation interesting and, considering the ideas of the young man cited above, wondered if this might give young people a sense of hope. All of the young people who took part in the focus group were unemployed at the time. Apart from one of the young women, none had any skills or qualifications. Although they appeared to be quite happy with their lot (the writer's perception), there are few opportunities for such young people at the present time. It should not be considered that the belief in reincarnation expressed by the young people suggests they feel that their lives are wasted. However, if the future in this life appears to have little opportunities, it could be that the promise of another life, another chance, could be quite comforting. Insufficient data was collected in this study to allow any speculation of how common the belief in reincarnation is among young people at the present time. It would also be difficult to know to what extent such beliefs vary and are shaped by variables, such as level of education, gender and social class. This speculation is of interest and social importance. How do the opportunities available to young people influence their beliefs about what happens after death and what is the purpose and significance of such beliefs? These are valuable questions for thanatologists to explore further.

By the time a young person reaches adolescence he/she has developed an awareness of the existential loneliness discussed earlier in this chapter. One of the storytellers aged twenty one recalls how:

"When I first realised that I wasn't a kid any more I had a terrible time. I put my parents through a terrible time. I really had terrible fears and I didn't know what they were for. I used to sit in my room and really wish that I could be a child again and be safe with my mother. And then again, I love my mother so, as I became aware of my death I also started to think about hers. I mean, it was bad enough knowing that as an adult I had to stand on my own two feet, but at least I could turn to her for some things. But I mean, my mum had always been there, she was just there. And I really went through quite a morbid period when I started to realise that one day she would be gone. I used to worry about her such a lot. And when I heard of people her age who died I'd find myself watching her. But in one sense it was a good thing because it made me strong. Strong in the sense that, although I found it hard to face the fact that I was

growing up, once I came to terms with it I felt strong. And as for my mother, well I'm not clingy any more, but I do appreciate her more, before I just took her for granted."

When discussing adolescence and death, we also need to consider the rather ambiguous position of adolescents in society. Adolescence is a fairly new concept in the life span in western society (Corr and McNiel, 1986; Gordon, 1986; Kastenbaum, 1986). To understand the meanings young people assign to life and death, we need to consider the historical and contemporary position of adolescence more generally.

In recent years, several writers have taken an interest in the intellectual and emotional changes that become apparent during adolescence and link these with young people's increasing awareness of death. For a dated, but nevertheless thought-provoking, collection of these discussions, the reader is referred to 'Adolescence and Death' (Corr and McNiel, 1986) from which much of the information included in the discussion to follow, has been derived. In this text, writers such as Kastenbaum and Gordon challenge the dominant and popular assumptions about adolescents that prevail in modern society, ie. those underpinning the 'storm and stress theories.' Gordon (1986) also discusses the increasingly worrying problem of adolescent suicide. One of the young men interviewed had quite strong views on suicide. However, he did not adopt a dogmatic or judgmental attitude when putting forward his views:

"To me that's the worst crime against yourself and anyone else. I mean life is to be lived, just because it's there really. I know that we have been talking about the meaning of life and death. But no matter what we think, life is given and it should be lived as long as it's there. Even if it's not easy, you can't give up on it. And all of our experiences, the good and the bad we have for a reason. The reasons might not be clear when we are going through them, but it will be one day. That's the one death anyway that you definitely can prevent. You can stop yourself from killing yourself! That's maybe the only power about life and death you ever really have. Mind you, maybe that's why some do it. And if that's the only

control they have, maybe it's wrong to blame them for taking it."

Gordon has provided an interesting analysis of the link between the adolescent's increasing sense of self and his/her developing sexuality, and an increasing awareness of death. He draws on Aries (1974) who reported that, during the Romantic period, orgasm was considered to be a kind of 'little death', because of the loss of self this involved. This link between sexuality and death has been made by other workers, such as Kastenbaum (1988), Baldwinson (1996) and Gorer (1965). Gordon, however, links the two themes to risk behaviour. He points out that many of the emotions and sensations that are part of both risk and sexual experience are very similar, ie. exhilaration, sensations of danger and testing of physical limits. This 'flirting with death', engaged in by some adolescents, has also been observed and commented on by Corr and McNeil (1986). They consider that it may provide young people with a sense of control of the two things over which they have little control; their developing sexuality and their mortality.

In his contribution, Kastenbaum is respectful and positive in his discussion of adolescence. He acknowledges the specific needs that adolescents may have for systems of support after a bereavement, or to help them to come to terms with the concept of death. However, he questions whether or not adults dismiss too readily, the important moral and philosophical questions raised by adolescents. Gordon suggests that much of the so called 'rebellious' behaviour exhibited by young people is part of a self-fulfilling prophecy and draws on the work of Bandura to support this view. Bandura wrote:

"If a society labels its adolescents as 'teenagers' and expects them to be rebellious, unpredictable, sloppy and wild in their behaviour, and if this picture is repeatedly reinforced by the mass media, such cultural expectations may well force adolescents into the role of rebel."

(Bandura; cited by Gordon, 1986)

Holland, writing more generally about adolescence in 1975, raised similar questions. She argued that the patronising assumption of many adults, especially psychologists, that a wide ranging concern with philosophical and political questions is to be expected in adolescence, is really just a way of dismissing some of the important issues that the latter raise. Rather than taking such questions seriously, she argues, many adults tell themselves that such concerns are little more than 'symptoms' of a condition we call adolescence, a way of saying 'well what can you expect?' In this way, adults protect themselves from having to confront the issues raised by adolescents because they feel uncomfortable about them. In considering the social conditions that have led to the different forms of loss, experienced by people of all ages in the twentieth century, perhaps we should ask why the concerns of adolescents are often taken so lightly.

Prior to our discussion of the meaning assigned to death by many adolescents, it is useful to consider the historical development of the concept of adolescence. Gordon writes that adolescence is a fairly recent classification and was caused by a number of influences. Technological developments were important because more sophisticated technology increased the need for a well-educated work force. The number of years spent in education was another increasingly important factor. Increased educational opportunities for all, starting with secondary, then further, then higher education, were part of the move towards a more egalitarian society which post war politicians, such as Bevin dreamed of (Turner and Rennell, 1989). Such changes led to the need for a period of time between childhood and adulthood, during which individuals could prepare for the challenges of adult life by developing vocational and life skills. This period became known as adolescence (Gordon, 1986).

The creation of adolescence caused many problems, the most difficult for society and the individuals concerned, being the ambiguous position in which adolescents found themselves (Corr and McNeil, *op cit*). Adults treat adolescents as 'bigger children', yet expect them to behave like young adults. One of the storytellers interviewed recalls that in early adolescence he felt 'conned':

"I mean, in a way its a bit of a con. You think when you are a kid that it will be great being an adult because you'll be free to do what you want. Because when I was a kid I

used to get fed up of adults telling me what to do. But then when I was about fourteen or fifteen I started to realise that once I grew up I'd have to do things by myself. I went through a period of feeling very alone and overwhelmed by the thought that I'd have to do things all by myself. And then for a time I felt a bit conned, I mean, what's so great about having all that responsibility? I think that growing up, and especially that period when you begin to realise, when it starts to dawn on you what being an adult actually means, well its hard.'

Ambivalence caused by the desire to grow to adulthood, while retaining the safety and security of childhood is understandable given that childhood and adulthood have benefits and disadvantages. The young person may experience this ambivalence at an early age. Simone De Beauvoir (1964) recalls how:

I would be stood up against the door frame in the hall and a pencilled line would be drawn level with the top of my head; the new line would be compared with an earlier one: I had grown two or three centimetres; they would congratulate me and I would swell with pride. But sometimes I felt frightened. The sunlight would be playing on the polished floor and the white enamelled furniture. I would look at Mama's armchair and think, 'I won't be able to sit on her knee any more if I keep on growing up.' Suddenly the future existed; it would turn me into another being, someone who would still be and yet no longer seem myself.

De Beauvoir, continues, recalling how, with some sense of regret, she began to accept the reality of her situation:

I kept on growing and I realised that my fate was sealed: 'I was condemned to be an outcast from childhood.'

The situation is probably complicated by the way in which many adolescents are expected to become involved in activities that are considered to be part of the adult world. War offers such an example. Most of the young men who fought and lost their lives in the First, Second and Vietnam Wars were adolescents. Apparently, gender roles significantly influence young people's sense of identity and, in turn, their feelings about adult responsibilities and death. One of my storytellers, a young man aged eighteen years recalls:

"That's one thing I do remember. I first started thinking about war when I saw news reports about war on the telly. Then it was a few things really, doing history at school, knowing that a lot of the old men I know have lived through a war. I started then worrying a lot about war because being a lad, well to be a man, that meant that if a war started I might have to go and fight. Funnily enough I was thinking or coping with two things at the same time when I look back on it. The thought of death and being a man and thinking about all the responsibilities that being a man entails. War and the thought of any kind of cruelty has always upset me. I don't know if it was the fear of being killed or the fear of having to kill. Really, honestly, both upset me just as much . . . I can't say that this stopped me wanting to be a man. But it did make me feel that, in the event of a war, I'd be disadvantaged as a man in that I'd be expected to go. And another thing, when I was very young and I saw reports of war or violence on the telly, like in Northern Ireland, I sort of comforted myself by telling myself that the adults would sort it out. Sometimes I'd get a bit impatient with them, but on the whole I thought, the grown ups will sort it out. Then as a got older I realised that I was about to become one of the adults who would have to sort it out. And I didn't feel that I could cope with that kind of responsibility. It was very hard."

In this extract, the young storyteller struggles with some quite complex and important issues. He recognises that there is an increasing responsibility as he approaches adulthood to take some political position, rather than just opt out. The author knows that the young man quoted above is very opposed to violence. In the event of a war, he may have to adopt the role of conscientious objector. Discussing this matter further after the focus view interview, the young man admitted that it worried him that, if put to the test, he might not have the courage to make a stand. He admitted that for him such responsibilities seem overwhelming. He did, however, acknowledge the need and the willingness to come to terms with them. He is also aware that taking a such a political position requires courage. In the opinion of the author, the thoughts and opinions expressed by the young people interviewed suggests a grasp of complex issues that makes it impossible to dismiss their views as 'immature.

Kastenbaum suggests that many of the questions young people ask about life and death, stem from their direct or indirect experience of events, such as the Vietnam War. Holland considers it was partly the impact of the Second World War that influenced the student political activity, which increased steadily in the years after 1945. During the 1950s and 1960s, adolescent political activities, and the accompanying cry for revolution, were viewed by parents, teachers and society at large, with 'kindly' tolerance. However, as student numbers grew, the call for revolution became stronger. There was a growing concern that politically active groups of young people posed a serious threat to the *status quo*. Gradually, tolerance gave way to an authoritarian attitude that, although not envisaged by Holland when writing in 1975, was to culminate in the evolution of the New Right. Holland concludes her 1975 paper by criticising the way that the concerns of so many adolescents are dismissed by adults and, in particular, by psychiatrists. She argues that:

> *'To argue that inner conflicts can only be solved intra-psychically, is to employ a theory that is only half a theory. Only half of the dialectic between inner and outer worlds. The beliefs and actions of adolescents must be seen within a social, historical process in which it becomes apparent that many of today's adolescents are growing up to see external reality, to interpret it, and to try to change it. Their demand for revolution in the outside world is not reducible to 'really' a response to their newly emergent and revolutionising instinctual demands. But rather, these psychic energies of adolescence can be powerful allies in a social revolution from which many of their elders have opted out.'*

Gordon also challenges the assumption that the moral and social questions posed by adolescents reflect 'inner conflicts' and as such, are simply symptoms of young people's 'up and down' moods. He considers that such questions reflect logical reasoned argument rather than emotionality. Gordon also points out that in mid life, many older people revisit the issues that had concerned them in youth. Indeed, this is becoming so well-recognised that some theorists now refer to another classification in the lifespan called 'middlescence' — a kind of second adolescence. If such concerns are, indeed, revisited by people in mid life then it is more difficult to argue that the concerns of youth represent little more than immature idealism.

Becker (1991) notes that, as young people become aware of death, they also discover a need to attach some meaning to life. For the young, such meaning goes beyond the concerns of adults as they become swamped with the practicalities of securing a career, a home, some stability. It is because of these concerns that one young woman, present during the focus group interviews, asserted:

"To be honest I don't think about death so much as I do about life. I mean, I've got a lot to think about in the next few years, what with hoping to get to college and do my degree or my nursing training whichever. And just the day to day living, worrying about paying the bills and so forth, those things worry me more at the moment than thinking about death. I've got my life to live and to be honest I want to live it. I'll think about death when I'm old and I've got no choice. Now, I want to think about living."

Adolescents may sometimes challenge the values of adults, questioning the principles underpinning the materialistic world in which we live. In doing so, they are saying 'there has to be more purpose, more meaning to life than this'. This questioning of dominant values is implicit in the comments made by one of the interviewees, a young woman:

"College, yes that seems a good idea, but what for? I mean there's no jobs even if you have a good education. I don't know what I want. I'd like children someday, I'd love a child because then I'd have something worthwhile to live for, someone to care for. But for now I just want to be happy and live a little. I'd probably be more keen on getting a job if I could get one with decent pay, or going to college if I thought I could get a better job. But the way

*things are at the moment . . . well you might as well just
enjoy life while you can."*

This causes conflict. Kubler-Ross (1983) argues that, cons-
ciously and unconsciously, parents in western society are increasingly falling into the trap of measuring their children's
worth in terms of their academic and career achievements,
rather than their value as human beings. It is understandable,
in a competitive world, that parents should encourage and
value their children's academic development, but Kubler-Ross
also notes that too much pressure from parents can make it
difficult for children to feel unconditionally loved. Indeed,
parents may forget their unconditional love for their children,
sometimes with disastrous results. Kitzinger and Kitzinger
(1989) comment on the increasing pressure on young people to
achieve. They discuss the case of a mother who beat her child
to death because he had a poor school report. Later, the
mother killed herself while in jail, leaving a letter in which she
expressed deep remorse.

As far as the young people interviewed for this study
were concerned, life was about living for the moment. This
may be due to the few opportunities they have at the present
time. In such a context, the idea of living for the moment may
be a coping strategy developed to manage what they perceive
to be the reality of the situation:

*"I can't say that I have any big ambitions. In fact I think
that these days you need to be very careful not to bring
yourself unhappiness by wanting more than you're ever
likely to get . I think sometimes, 'Oh I'd like to do this and
I'd like to do that.' But then I think 'wait a minute.'
(laughs) I do think it's a good idea improving yourself.
But to go to college nowadays thinking you'll
automatically get a better job I think that's a very big
mistake. Because unemployment is high now for just
about everyone, no matter what qualifications you've got.
To me, you should improve yourself to improve yourself if
you know what I mean. Like, if I did a course, it would
have to be something that I'd enjoy doing while I'm doing
it and it would have to improve me some way. I wouldn't
do it just for the sake of getting a better job. You might get*

a better job, but you're just as likely to not get one. So why ask for disappointment and unhappiness?"

From this study, it appears that, for many young people, finding some purpose to life is linked to the process of coming to terms with their increasing awareness of their mortality. In a very private way, they challenge the value some parents and many adults place on academic success. One young man did see some value in working hard towards a goal. But his thoughts did not include any consideration of further education. His aspirations were actually very modest:

"I haven't got any big ambitions. I'd like a nice home, nothing too posh, just the right size for a family and comfortable, and the basic things like good heating, a nice telly, a nice car, just big enough to get me and my family around. I mean, it seems sometimes that it would be nice to have pots of money. But from what I've seen it doesn't always bring people happiness. Sometimes it can bring a lot of unhappiness in fact because you take things for granted if you can get them easy like. If I had lots of money, I'd keep it. What I mean is, if I won the lottery I would take the money and spend it on the things like I've said I'd like. But if I don't win the lottery, well I'm willing to work hard to get what I want. But to me the most important thing of all is to have no worries. I suppose that's not likely, but that is to me the most important thing."

The modest aspirations of the young people interviewed may be due to the high unemployment recorded at the present time. But this is not necessarily the case for all. One of the adult men interviewed, held similar values and has done for most of his life:

"I can't say that I have any big ambitions. Just live for today, enjoy a few gigs (the man is a musician who plays in a local band) *and just live for the moment and don't let things get on top of you. After all, in a hundred years from now, who will care about the things you worried about today. So live for today, enjoy life and try not to worry."*

The death of a peer, particularly if it is due to suicide, can have a profound effect on young people. This can make exploration of questions, such as those discussed by the young people interviewed, seem all the more important. When such a thing happens, adolescents would probably benefit from the support of adults. Corr and McNeil argue that, in western society generally, parents try to protect adolescents, as they do young children, from all aspects of death and dying. This is a problem Gordon argues, particularly when we consider that media representations of death and dying are rarely tender and compassionate, but rather violent or over-romantic. Alteg (1989) has explored in some detail violent representations of death that are part of modern youth culture, in particular popular music. He contrasts the various ways that death is represented in young people's music, commenting not just on its presentation as violent and unpleasant but also on those which present sympathetic images of old age and dying, such as the Beatles' 'When I'm Sixty Four'. He considers that popular music provides a valuable source for counsellors, teachers and youth workers working with young people to explore death. Alteg points out that more research needs to be done to develop a deeper understanding of the way music can be used to help young people come to terms with death.

In our concluding chapter we will discuss the support systems that can be developed to help young people come to terms with death and bereavement, including death education. Many thanatologists consider that death education is an encouraging development and will better enable adults, educators and health care workers to prepare young people for the challenges of adult life. However, having considered the need so many adolescents have to impart some meaning to life, it seems relevant to conclude with reference to the view of Gordon, who argues that a future without hope leads to death of the soul and, sometimes, to suicide. We need to consider the social climate that exists at the time of writing this book, rising unemployment and a climate in which even the most talented and enterprising of our youth cannot be confident of future security in their chosen profession. Many of the young people from the community in Halliwell cannot get jobs. Few, if any, are lazy or lacking in motivation. Yet, during the interview, they told of how they are penalised if they claim unemployment benefit for too long. Such young people cannot be described as lazy in these circumstances, they are simply realistic. What is the point of looking for jobs that do not exist? A recent campaign launched by the government encourages people to report those who are claiming benefits to which they are not entitled. The danger of this policy is that it may be abused, providing a means for people to get even with those who annoy or anger them rather than revealing fraudulent benefit claims. In contemporary society, young people are now denied a future. Instead of offering support and prospects for improvement, society 'punishes' them because they have no future.

In recent years the cry for revolution has been silenced. Is this because things are so good that such a cry is no longer needed? This seems unlikely. In some respects this is very sad. For it was not the cry of previous generations for revolution that was important (and a revolution need not be violent) but rather, the energy, hope and optimism of youth, that was the driving force behind such a cry — a belief that a better world was possible. We have lost not only the cry for revolution, but the belief in its credibility. Increasing technology means that many young people will never know what it is to have paid employment. One way to help young people regain hope, may be to change the concept of 'success'. We should abandon the idea that it is shameful not to have a job and explore new ways in which people can make positive contributions to their communities. In Bolton we have a town with a rich cultural heritage and an excellent community education service, at the level of both further and higher education. These need to be protected by the people of Bolton, and should be utilised to improve the quality of life for all. To fulfil this purpose, it may be necessary to change the emphasis of education and community services. They may need to change from an approach concerned only with preparing people for careers, to one that prepares them for life, inside and outside the spheres of paid employment. This may give people a basis on which to build a sense of purpose into their lives, to take pride in themselves, their potential and their achievements. What kind of future do we want for our children?

Chapter 3

Children's exposure to representations of death and dying in the media

This chapter explores the effect that exposure to images of death in the media has on children and young people. Given that in the present death is more likely to occur in hospital, the media has become the main source of information about death and dying. It is useful, therefore, to gain some insight into the effect such images and portrayals have on young people. This chapter draws on interviews conducted by one of the authors with young people from Bolton. The aim of these interviews was to assess to what extent media images of death and dying influence young people's perceptions and behaviour. The interviews also attempt to establish whether or not this group of young people share the concerns of the writers who have expressed misgivings at portrayals of death and dying in the media. Much of the writing and work conducted by academics on the effects of the media on young people has been quite negative.

Children's exposure to portrayals of death in the media has been a source of debate and concern in psychology for a number of years. The main concern has been that, if children are continually exposed to violent portrayals of death, this could encourage them to express aggressive behaviour and attitudes which hold that human life is 'cheap'. Gordon (1986) writes that children are constantly exposed to media images of death as violent, distant or unrealistically beautiful. Rarely, he comments, is death ever presented with sensitivity or compassion. Alteg (1986) has also noted that many of the themes in the popular music of youth are full of violence, suicide or accidental death caused by overdose. Ageing is also presented by the media as distasteful and to be avoided at all costs. Kitzinger and Kitzinger (1989) have argued that violence on television can be quite worrying for a child. This is because in most action films it is always the 'baddy' that gets killed. This can lead a child to believe that death comes as a punishment for misbehaving. Some support for this view was suggested by the points made by one of the young men interviewed:

> *"As a matter of fact, the deaths that really upset me the most on television are the violent deaths. Its the injustice of it really. I can't put my finger on what I am trying to say but, its the kind of humiliation of it really. Violent death is, well there's no family, and its kind of, the last feeling that person may have had before they died was hate, you know. I think it must be very sad when a person dies and the last thing they have is hate, hate coming from themselves or from someone else, the person who is killing them. I must admit that does upset me. And when its the 'baddy' that dies violently, it seems to be all right. But its not all right. No one deserves to die like that no matter what they have done."*[1]

The young man does recognise that there can be an aura of retribution about some violent deaths in the media. But he is far from a passive observer who absorbs information in an uncritical way. Indeed, the fact that he is able to critique what he sees on film presents a problem for social scientists who express concern about the effects that violence in the media can have on young people. If people are able to criticise what they see or hear, it seems unlikely that they can be totally influenced by it. However, it is important to note that the interviews were conducted with adolescents and, from the data gathered for this study, it is not possible to assess the effect that portrayals of death could have on young children. Even if it is the case that media images of death and dying, particularly images of violent death, can have negative effects on children, one of the young men interviewed drew attention to the difficulties parents have in trying to ensure that their children are not exposed to them:

> *"I'm not sure that seeing violence on TV really effects children, its more who they knock around with. But even if it did, I think its very hard for parents. Mine were dead against me watching anything like that but I just used to*

---

1   This young man was 19 years of age when interviewed in 1996

find out which of my friends could watch whatever it was that I wanted to watch. And as for videos, you can always find out where they (the parents) have hidden them. I think that when your parents stop you from watching films that everyone else is watching, then you just want to watch it more, especially if all your friends have seen it. Its not really because you want to watch the film, like, because you think you will enjoy it. It's cos you want to be like your friends. I think that rather than stop you watching it, parents should watch it with you. Really, its pointless trying to stop them because they will get to see it one way or another — I did anyway." [2]

Much of the work that social scientists have done on death and violence in the media, appears to be based on the assumption that such portrayals are quite a recent phenomenon, a development that ran parallel with that of film and television. Yet there is evidence from historical sources to confirm that children have been exposed to violent, unrealistic and sometimes quite horrific portrayals of death for much longer than we are inclined to think. In the eighteenth and nineteenth centuries, for example, there was a theory that violent fairy tales could warp children's minds (Kitzinger and Kitzinger, 1989). During the war years, children were exposed to images of violence, the threat of violent death and bereavements caused by the deaths of family members.

After World War Two, there was a reported increase in juvenile crime that, understandably, caused a great deal of public concern. Generally, this was a time when there was a lot of public dissatisfaction and, indeed, some politicians feared that there might be a revolution. The anticipated revolution did not happen, but it did become more common for people from all walks of life to challenge authority. The main target of criticism were sections of traditional establishments, such as the school and the church.[3] This challenge to authority came about partly because of some of the atrocities caused by the

---

2   Young man aged 21 years when interviewed in 1996.
3   See the bibliography for some secondary sources of information on this.

war. In academic life, this was a challenge that was generally accepted and even given approval. After the war there were several famous studies conducted on the authoritarian personality and on conformity and obedience. The aim of such research was to try to come to some understanding of why people can sometimes commit terrible atrocities because in their view they were just following orders.[4]

A general concern for the social order and the state of humanity may have increased anxiety about juvenile delinquency. One attempt to find an explanation was Bowlby's Theory of Maternal Deprivation (1969), which proposed that the presence and full-time care of the mother was essential for the well-being of the child's mental health. It was a convenient and useful theory. The accusatory finger for the cause of juvenile delinquency could point at working mothers, rather than the effects of war. There was also a concern to avoid the high rates of unemployment that followed the First World War. In this context, Bowlby's theory provided an ideal justification for closing the state nurseries that had provided childcare for working women during the war, forcing many to give up paid employment. Such a wide scale withdrawal of a public service led to a substantial financial saving for the government. This was accepted by the country as a whole because of the view that working mothers were probably responsible for the high rates of juvenile delinquency. The stereotype of the pathetic 'latch key kid' was increasingly promoted. The disapproval of working mothers implicit within this image, must have made life difficult for such women.[5]

In Bolton, the increasing social (middle-class) disapproval for children taking on adult responsibilities within the home must have changed their position in the family. Previous work conducted by one of the authors revealed that in Bolton in the recent past, children were expected to help out in the

---

4   An overview of some of this work can be found in any introduction to Psychology textbook. The Gross book *Psychology: The Science of Mind and Behaviour* is a particularly good source.

5   For further reading on these issues, see the bibliography.

home from a very early age.[6] This was because their mothers had to work. None of the women who reported this felt that being given such responsibilities as children caused them any harm. Rather than blaming working mothers, perhaps we should consider to what extent the experiences of war were responsible for the rise in juvenile delinquency.

Interviews conducted with older women who had experienced the war, plus data from other sources, suggest that children were not spared from exposure to the propaganda against the Germans. Indeed, it appears that they were encouraged to hate them, and even consider them as less than human (Kenny, 1994). Such propagand techniques must have had an impact on children's perceptions of death and, more importantly, their attitudes towards the value of human life. In his autobiographic collections of the war years, Ashton writes:

> *'it was a time when kids were conditioned to violence, conflict and war'*

and that:

> *'the kids reacted to war as they do to all adult enthusiasms. They couldn't have cared less about the rights and wrongs, so long as our side won.'*

(Ashton, 1982)

In the weeks leading up to and after VE day, children were also exposed to effigies of Hitler, in itself another form of violence. One Bolton paper displayed[7] a photograph of munitions workers who had strung up an effigy of Hitler over machines in a Bolton engineering works. It could be argued that, given the pain and suffering caused by the war, it was understandable that many people would want to ridicule Hitler. The munitions workers may have suffered bereavement through the deaths of several relatives and friends during the war. For many people, this was often the case (Kenny, 1994). Such

---

6   Research conducted by Kenny (1994) on women's experiences of working in the textile industry. *Cotton Everywhere*. Aurora Press, Bolton.
7   The Bolton Evening News, Saturday, May 5th, 1945 *'That Man Again'*.

behaviour may have been therapeutic, providing a safe release for the anger that is a common response to a bereavement. The danger was that such ridicule could, instead, lead to a focus on thoughts of revenge, ie. 'an eye for an eye'? As Gandhi pointed out, this just leaves the whole world blind.

This discussion is not concerned with passing judgment on such behaviour. The authors are by no means sure of the answers to the questions raised, but would, instead, invite readers to consider the topic. These are important matters for reflection, if only because by examining them, we could at least recognise and accept the basic humanity of humankind.

By using the effigy as an example, there is evidence in the literature to suggest that, in laughing at the things which cause pain, stress or fear of death, these can be rendered harmless, and such laughter may well be therapeutic.[8] Freud (1961) referred to the tendency to laugh at death as 'gallows humour'. At the same time, there is evidence to suggest that if we dehumanise others, it is much easier to inflict harm on them. Effigies do dehumanise and are used as sources of amusement all the time. How many of us stop to consider when we help our children build a Guy Fawkes and put it on the bonfire every year, that we are celebrating the horrific torture and execution of a human being?

In relating violent portrayals of death to people's lived experience of it, can a connection be established between the two. If so, what is it? According to research, it appears that, if people are frequently exposed to violence and death, their feelings of concern are rendered less sensitive. This is the case for both adults and children. A Bolton paper in 1943 reported that after three and a half years of war, the people of Bolton had ceased to carry gas masks, and this lack of concern applied to men, women[9] and probably children. Some of the people interviewed by one of the authors reported that they soon grew tired of having to carry their gas masks around.

Part of the apparent indifference towards the war expressed by some children, may have stemmed from the fact

8   See Kenny *et al*, 1998a.
9   *The Bolton Evening News*, February 10th, 1943.

that they did not experience the level of horror which they had anticipated. Childs (1982) remembered hiding with his family in the cellar in Bolton during the bombing of Manchester and wrote of his experiences, thus:

> *'the reality of our situation in that moment of genuine terror was far less dramatic than we had supposed. No bombs had fallen on our street, no one had been killed.'*

He recalls that no one in his immediate family was killed during the war. So for him and many other people, fear of childhood diseases such as TB, diphtheria and bronchitis were far more frightening than any threat presented by the war. People of any age may cope with the experience of war by adopting strategies that were identified by the psychoanalyst, Freud, as those of denial or repression. When experiencing very traumatic and stressful situations, people push their unpleasant memories to the back of their minds. The mind is not always successful at pushing fearful thoughts and memories away from its consciousness, and these fears are frequently expressed in other ways. This is suggested by the autobiographic account of William van de Zand (1982) in 'Children and War'. Van de Zand, writing of the American bombing of Nymegen, a town in the Netherlands which had been mistaken by the allies for a German town, recalls how:

> *'That day I saw many dead and wounded, but somehow it did not touch me'*

and that:

> *'The bombing and shelling increased, but we didn't even bother to go into the cellar any more.'*

Despite van de Zand's reported indifference to the bombings, he writes in the same paragraph:

> *'The shortages got worse and more and more friends and members of our family disappeared into concentration camps. Rumours about life in the camps often kept me awake at night, trembling with fear, if ever my father... or how would I cope? Punishment for resistance workers became increasingly gruesome, and hostages, even young people, were executed without trial.'*

(van de Zand, 1982)

Despite reports of indifference to the war, evidence from other sources suggests that children may have been more afraid than they were prepared to admit. One Bolton paper, reporting on the excitement of school children in the town due to the coming VE day celebrations, also reported that children were:[10]

> *'Too full of war news to give their mind to anything else. A contributing factor in unsettling the children, teachers believe, are the horror films of Belsen and Buchenwald. Children openly discuss the more terrible scenes and refer teachers to them if an appropriate opportunity arises during a lesson.'*

In *Chapter 1* we referred briefly to the opinion of some of the older women interviewed that bereaved children were not sufficiently supported during World War Two. Kitzinger and Kitzinger (*op cit*) have commented on the lack of support that appears to be available for children during a war or conflict situation. They suggest that this may be due to the fact that the adults are so overwhelmed with the scale of death, they tell themselves that children are resilient and will bounce back. However, evidence from numerous research studies suggests that children who lose a parent in a conflict situation can suffer terrible emotional problems. They may continue to display symptoms of behavioural disturbance for up to four years or longer after the loss (Van-Eerdewegh *et al*, 1985; Elizur and Kauffman, 1983).

Some practitioners have observed a condition called post traumatic stress disorder (PTSD) in some people who have experienced the traumas of war. Research into children's reactions to stressful situations have reported cases of PTSD in children as young as eight years old. The symptoms expressed by such children are identical to those observed in adults who suffer from the condition (Yule, 1989; Smith and Pennells, 1995). The effects of witnessing the violent death of a parent can have a strong negative and long-term impact on a child's mental health. Dyregrow and Kingsley (1991) cite a case described by Bergan (1958) of a four-year-old girl who had

---

10   *The Bolton Evening News,* May 7th, 1945.

witnessed the murder of her parents. Following this experience, she developed a game in which she painted her hands red and imitated the action of stabbing herself with a paint brush. Terr (1983) found that children who witness violent scenes can lose faith in their own future. At a common-sense level, it could be argued that such findings are only to be expected. However, recent work, conducted by researchers working with the Centre for Conflict Studies at the University of Ulster, suggests that the effects of experiencing conflict situations are not always clear cut and care should be taken in making assumptions. Researchers at the Centre for Conflict Studies found it difficult to separate the effects of social deprivation and exposure to conflict situations. Dyregrow (1991) found that children traumatised by such experiences can sometimes develop an altruistic attitude to life. It appears from this study, that witnessing violent incidents can actually increase rather than decrease a child's ability to empathise and care for others.

Many of the children who experienced the Blitz came from poorer, inner city areas. The poverty and ill health of British children from these areas become apparent during the 1939 evacuation. Foster parents who took in evacuated children were shocked at the obvious poverty the latter had experienced. Other officials and foster parents were very concerned about the high level of ill health they found in those who they took into their homes, and newspapers of the time, reported conflict situations which arose between the natural and foster parents. However, the author has not identified any reports which suggest that the majority of evacuated children were deviant or violent[11].

It would appear that there are many ways in which the lived experience of violence can influence children. Long-term effects can be very complex and unpredictable. To what extent do lived experiences of violence and death relate to fictitious portrayals of it? The aim of this discussion is not to advocate

---

11   This issue is discussed in greater depth in Kenny *et al*, 1998c, *Thanatology of War*. The perceptions some foster parents had of the evacuees and their families could be quite negative.

children's exposure to violence, but rather to explore the result such exposure has, and whether or not children affected will suffer long-term damage. Discussion of the effects of violence in the media continues with an exploration of historical portrayals of similar issues. Prior to the introduction of mass media, these were presented in the form of children's literature and we draw on the work of Dixon (1989) who has conducted research in this area. Later, we will relate some contemporary, theoretical perspectives on this issue to data gathered by one of the authors during her interviews with young people.

Dixon's study provides an analysis of portrayals of death in Victorian children's periodicals. Her research suggests that Victorian children were just as exposed to, what Gorer has called, the 'pornography of death' in the magazines of the time, as the children of today view on film and television. Dixon's study offers an interesting challenge to the popular belief that it is a recent trend for children to be exposed to violence and death by the media. The means by which such material is conveyed may have changed, but her work provides a useful source for understanding how children during the Victorian era were socialised into accepting life and death ideologies, and 'appropriate' ways of grieving. Dixon compared the portrayal of death in two types of Victorian children's journals, those produced by religious affiliations and those produced for commercial gain. The journals produced by religious groups used the concept of death as a device to shape young readers moral characters. In such publications, death could be presented as just desserts for some male villain or fickle young woman. For this 'breed' an unspeakable fate awaited in the after life. The child death bed scene was a popular portrayal of death in such magazines. In such scenarios the 'good' children 'withered' away, having fallen victim to one of the many contagious diseases of the time.

Dixon reports that these scenes were very descriptive, focusing almost entirely on the dying child. Such children, although apparently drawing their last breath, never lacked the required lung capacity to 'gasp' the famous last word. The witness to these last words was usually the mother, whose presence at the scene, Dixon notes, appears to have been only for this purpose. Although sad at a superficial level, such scenes were ultimately 'happy' because the 'good' child was going to a 'better' place.

The second group of journals examined by Dixon, those produced for commercial gain, caused religious groups much concern because of their perceived potential to encourage young people, especially working-class youths, into lives of depravity and crime. The motives for producing each group of journals were very different. Despite this, Dixon comments, the contents were much the same, each having its quota of mutilation, gore and horror.

Dixon cites examples of the villains depicted in religious journals, such as 'The Children's Friend.' These included deceitful Alfred, who fell off a cliff, and a youth who drowned because he failed to attend divine worship, preferring instead to splash around in the local lodge. In each group of journals, gory stories were accompanied by even gorier illustrations. These included an array of mutilated bodies with guts and blood pouring out, of decapitation, and of young boys playing football with severed heads (Dixon, *op cit*). Even mourning cards of the time could carry, despite the obvious grief of the bereaved parents, a warning message with moral undertones. The following verse is taken from a mourning card that forms part of the local archives' library at Bolton:

> *'In Remembrance of the late Ellen Barker — died on the 8th instant, in her 28th year and on this day was interred at Horwich Church on September, 1855.*
>
> *My time is short as here you see reader prepare to follow me.'*

In other words, 'don't waste time, there's little enough of it'.

Towards the end of the nineteenth century, the significance of death rituals became increasingly important. Journals provided increasingly complex descriptions of grieving behaviours and features in young girls' journals, presented the latest and most fashionable mourning dress. Dixon reports that the journals she examined were extremely popular during the nineteenth century. If this is correct, they may have had a powerful effect on children's perceptions of death and bereavement. Such influences may well have continued into adult life. The frequent portrayal of violent images could have been detrimental to the children who were exposed to them. But at the time such journals were considered a useful way of shaping the child's moral character. They also aimed to prepare children for their own possible death. Dixon's analysis of such journals has more to offer than an understanding of why death rituals were so important during the Victorian era. Such analysis also offers a challenge to dominant child ideology. Concerns of whether or not children should be educated about death, and if so, in what way, are based on assumptions about children's differing intellectual abilities.[12]

Approaches to the introduction of death education in schools will be discussed in our concluding chapter. Meanwhile, we consider the modern portrayals of death in the media. In this discussion we have focused mainly on the portrayal of violent death. We acknowledge the importance of points made by Gordon (1986), for example, who has expressed disapproval of the media's tendency to present death in overly romantic and unrealistic ways. Indeed, two of the young people interviewed for this study made spontaneous responses to this aspect of death on television. They held the view that romantic portrayals of death in the media could be harmful, but not necessarily:

Respondent 1:*"I think that for very young children making it seem all peaceful and romantic can be bad, well, I think so because when I was a little kid, I used to day dream sometimes about dying to get back at my parents you'll be sorry when I'm dead and all that sort of thing . . . If my parents made me angry I'd imagine this great death bed scene and imagine my parents crying and asking my forgiveness, and I'd be really kind and say its all right mum, you didn't know when you didn't let me go to the pictures*

12   See *Chapter 2.*

*that I was dying and that was the very last
chance I had to go* (laughs). *But the thing is, I
never really thought about the fact that once
I'm dead, I'll not be able to gloat at everyone
being sorry. . . and it never went on to be
anything but a day dream, and of course I
didn't die, that's the thing, on telly, no one
really dies."*[13]

Respondent 2:*"It is true that when sick children die on
television, they do get all the attention, it can
seem like a way of getting attention, and it all
seems dead good because like, everyone's there,
caring about you and . . . I think it can seem a
dead good thing, to be really kind and forgive
people, I think that's something we can all
think about though, that kind of you'll be sorry
when I'm gone its like, when we feel taken for
granted really. But I don't think anyone would
want it to really happen. Its like when you're at
school and you really wish you could be ill then
you can skive off. But when you really are ill,
it's horrible. I don't think that thinking about
something and doing it are the same at all, its
just a day dream, and its not the same anyway,
when you watch telly and some ones dying its
like, the chance for a good cry really, and you
enjoy it lets face it. I cry when no one's looking.
But if you really are crying for something bad
that's happened to you, well its awful, it's not
the same, crying for a good cry and crying 'cos
your in real sort of grief, it's not the same. I
think it can be good for you. I mean, if I'm
really fed up I'll sometimes buy a really sad
video so that I can have a good cry, it can help
you have a cry when you need it."*[14]

---

13   Young man aged 18 years at the time of his interview in 1995.
14   Young woman aged 21 years at the time of her interview in 1996.

There is possibly a gender difference indicated by the two accounts given above. The first respondent cited is a young man, the second a young women. Some writers argue that men and boys are discouraged from crying (Kitzinger and Kitzinger, 1989; Gilligan, 1993). Other writers have expressed concern over the difficulty many bereaved men have in crying. Because of this, men do not find it easy to work through the stages of grief. The young man cited discusses the child deathbed scene, but only in connection with his childhood day dreams — this is something he has left behind now. He does not mention crying at all. However, another young man suggested that feeling sad was acceptable, even if crying was barred:[15]

> *"A love scene where someone gets killed is good. Its good because then you can enjoy feeling sad and thinking 'oh dear, what a shame for them,' even though its only a film. It can be quite romantic — as long as its not real."*

Most of the young people interviewed made the point that feeling sad can be quite a pleasurable experience, as long as its not real. Feelings of sadness may relieve stress and help young men approximate something of the feelings described by the young woman interviewed. She, unlike the men, openly acknowledges that sometimes she enjoys a good cry. Furthermore, she finds this so beneficial that she will even borrow a video so that she can indulge herself. Her idea that crying can help relieve stress is supported by the research (Kenny, 1998a). So films with sad endings may provide a means of encouraging bereaved people to enter into the stages of grief. However, there is a relational aspect to this, so that it is not so much a death, but who dies in the film that matters:

> *"It depends on how important the person who dies is in the film. If they die early on in the film and there isn't an awful lot to their personality, if you see what I mean, well when they die that's the signal to get up and make a brew before the film moves on to something really good. But if it's someone important in the film and they die at the end*

---

15   Young man aged 18 years at the time of his interview in 1996.

*or even halfway through, then you'll hang on to see the
effect it has on everyone and what other people have to say
and all this. And the more important they are in the film
the more sad you feel. But that's just like real life isn't it. I
mean, if you read about someone dying in the paper you
don't know, well you do think, 'oh what a shame.' But
then you go on to read the next story, or start looking for
the telly page. But if its someone you know who dies and
you read about that in the paper, well that is different
again. Then you read every little word, and even that's
not enough, so then you start to ask other people and all
this. So its not so much a death on the telly that matters
so much, as how kind of used to the characters you are.*"[16]

It would seem that, despite the concern that media images of
death are unrealistic, some young people do consider them to
be representative of everyday life, ie. in the way that people
typically respond to them. To what extent and in what way do
violent portrayals of death influence young people? This was
another issue explored in the interviews. As acknowledged at
the beginning of this chapter, there is considerable research
evidence to suggest that exposure to violence on television and
film can encourage aggressive behaviour in children and
young people. Few of the young people interviewed agreed
with this evidence. The following is the response of one young
man to the question 'do you think that violence on TV
encourages aggressive behaviour?':

*"I don't think so. I don't think that it makes you get up
and want to be violent. I suppose it could do, but it doesn't
with me. When I've watched it, I've more or less forgotten
about it an hour or so later. I don't think that anyone
would watch a violent film just for the sake of it. It has to
have a good story, not just violence. Who would carry on
watching a crap film just for that, I mean that would be
boring.*"[17]

---

16 Young man aged 20 years at the time of his interview in 1995.
17 Young man aged 19 years at the time of his interview in 1996.

An alternative view of the effects of TV violence taken by some psychologists, is that media violence can provide a safe way to release natural feelings of aggression. The young person cited below, does not acknowledge that his enjoyment of violent films might be relieving his violent tendencies. Rather, he considers that the need for excitement is the most useful function.

> *"No, I don't think that films make you violent, or; well I just watch them for the excitement. It's not the violent act itself that is important, it's the film as a whole. You know the build up and all that, the suspense and when it makes you jump. You know, it starts off with the build up and you get more and more scared and then something happens to make you jump. I mean, when you think of some of the really scary or violent scenes, well they fit in with like, a story line. I love an exciting film, I like a bit of excitement. But I don't think people go out and do those things. It's like, I like a good car chase on telly, I really like that. But if I'm in a car in real life and the driver goes too fast, I shit myself, honest, I really am shit scared of real speed. People are just not like that. If they do, then I think that they must be a bit funny to begin with."* [18]

One of the young people interviewed did not feel that she could comment on the effects of violence on TV because:

> *"I don't watch it. I hide under the covers."*

Another young person expressed a concern that violent films and cartoons might cause younger children to accidentally injure each other during play. He felt that this was because such films promote unrealistic expectations of the harm that can be done when people fight, especially if they are only playing.

> *"I think those karate films are bad. I know when I was younger and I had watched films like karate kid I'd start playing at karate fighting with my friends. And we could easily have kicked each other and done some real harm. If our mums told us not to do it because we might hurt each*

18   Young man aged 18 years at the time of his interview in 1996.

other, we never believed them, because let's face it, no one gets really hurt on television. If we couldn't do it in front of our parents, we'd do it somewhere else."

Another young man expressed concern that children might develop the wrong values in life because of the way heroes are portrayed on television and film:

"I think that the main problem with telly programs is the way that the hero is always the one who goes around battering people. So you can get the idea that to be a hero you have to batter people all the time. It's not just that the hero always batters people or the fact that he always wins. It's the fact that he's all the other things that you think that you want to be when you grow up, you know, he's dead handsome, he has the best car, brainy. And that's another thing that I don't like, he usually shows how smart he is by making other people look stupid. So you get the idea that it's OK to make people look stupid. Like, making other people look stupid is the only way that you can make people take notice of how smart you are."

The concerns expressed by the young man quoted above are shared by many psychologists and are supported by research. Studies of TV violence, for example, have found that the hero is twice as likely to start the violence and that the victims are usually women or black people. Unrealistic presentations of the frequency in which the American police use their guns have also been found (Kitzinger and Kitzinger, *op cit*). However, not all the young people interviewed, agreed that media images of the tough hero could be harmful, and gave the following reasons:

"The hero doesn't always start the fights, he just always wins. And anyway, the hero can make some sick jokes sometimes, and that makes you laugh. I know it's not funny when people really die, but its fun to laugh at the ridiculous things some of the heroes say when people die in a film. I don't think that watching it on telly is the same. I mean, if some of the things that happened on television happened right here in this room, I'd be experiencing it wouldn't I? But the telly's there (pointing at the television in the room) and it's like looking into a

> *box. Its not real is it? I mean, you can switch it on, switch it off, turn it over, if it's a video you can pause it while you go off and make yourself a brew . . . you know what I mean? I've got control so it's not real. But if it happens like, in this room, like, someone breaks in and starts battering me, well I've got no control then have I? Well then obviously, I'd be terrified."[19]*

The young person cited above seems quite certain that he, and indeed everyone else, is perfectly capable of distinguishing between fact and fantasy. In the world of fantasy, it is safe to laugh at violence and death, and to engage in a little of the 'gallows humour' mentioned earlier in this discussion. However, as discussed in *Chapter 2*, young children are unable to distinguish between fact and fantasy. So how do such media images influence them? Another important point he raises, concerns the notion that with media violence the spectator has some control. A psychologist called Seligman described a condition that he referred to as Learned Helplessness. This is a condition developed by people and animals who constantly experience little or no control over their lives or environment. Learned helplessness is a frequent symptom of depressive illness and PTSD. An individual's level of control may be a dominant reason for the difference between media violence and a person's perceived experience of it.

Another young man also expressed concern for the way in which heroes are portrayed. He did not consider that all adolescents, or even young adults, could make such distinctions:

> *"I think that music can be just as bad as television to be honest. Especially this like danger music, the type that has this kind of rap to it. I call it danger music to be honest because I've been in the car when some of my friends are playing it and driving to it. And it really makes them bloody dangerous, and they like, act as if they are on a car chase, like the heroes who do it really well. Its like a gangster role, I can't explain it but it's as if they are playing a role. But for you who is in the*

passenger seat, the only role you play is the shit scared role."[20]

The young person quoted above has identified that music has the potential to bring out aggressive behaviour. He also goes beyond the way in which many of the young people interviewed defined violent behaviour to include driving behaviour. It may well be that, as he suggests, violent themes in rock music can predispose people to driving dangerously. He recognises that violent behaviour has an identity, its own unique image which young people buy into. It is not a part of what they are, but rather an act or role that is played by them. Within such a perception, accessories, such as a car, a car radio, the right clothes, all form a composite whole which we call violence. What he seems to be saying is that violent behaviour can be perceived as a culture in its own right, rather than the reflection of a culture. The danger of this is that we can all enter in and out of the culture, so far as our perceptions go. In this way, people can distance themselves from responsibility or accountability for their behaviour. It happens all the time in the name of professionalism; during a war in the name of patriotism. Two of the younger men interviewed refused to accept that anyone could commit a violent act without thinking about it, or of realising the consequences. They were keen to point out that people should take responsibility for their behaviour, the only exception being those who might have a mental health problem or very young children:

Respondent 1:*"I don't agree with all this about people being violent because of what they have seen on TV. I see violence on telly all the time and I don't go out with a stick afterwards to beat some one up.'*

Respondent 2:*"Yes I agree. I think that if TV does make you violent, well that's an excuse because you want an excuse. I think that these people who are violent because of the telly, they are like that to begin with, you know, they must be a bit funny.*

---

20   As above.

> *That can be a bit of a problem I suppose. People
> who see violent things on telly might get more
> ideas about how to be violent. But if they are
> that way inclined, they will find a way anyway.
> People are violent because they can't get what
> they want."*

Respondent 1:*"I think that young children can be a problem
to be honest. I don't think that they understand
that you can do real harm, but then, hurting
someone through play isn't the same thing I
don't think, as being violent. Being violent is
when you really want to hurt, but I think that
yes, there definitely can be a danger for
younger kids not realising the harm they can
do. . . I mean, at the end of the day the effects
are the same.'*

Another of the younger people present during this interview
decided to join in. He added:
> *"I think that people are violent to, to protect themselves.
> Like, I tend to walk away from trouble if I can but if
> someone hits me I'll probably hit him back. But if they are
> just calling me names, I'll walk away and ignore it."*

Respondent 1 added:
> *"Yes, I think that most people are violent to protect
> themselves, and also other things. Like, I think that
> people should be looking more at crime of all sorts
> through drugs or because a lot of people don't have
> enough money. That is a problem at all ages, from the kid
> who punches another kid to nick his computer. Or even,
> just because he's plain jealous, to the drug addict who
> needs a fix, or the poor sod on the street who has no food. I
> think that there is far, far more violence and crime due to
> social things like drugs or being poor, than you ever get
> through the telly. And that goes for people of all ages."*

Generally, most of the young people interviewed considered
that violence was caused by a variety of factors. These
included the need for personal protection, social problems and
lack of understanding by younger children of the harm certain
behaviours could cause. The young people also recognised that

media images of death and dying could be unrealistic but they did not consider this to be a real problem. Indeed, two of the young women interviewed considered that a sad film could be quite therapeutic. Several of the young people also commented that in both media and real life, the effect a death had on people depends on how well they know the deceased, regardless of whether this was a real or fictional character.

The final part of this chapter discussed the fact that children have seen presentations of violence and death for at least two hundred years. The purposes of such representations have been considered, drawing on historical research and interview material. We have also explored the relationship between people's lives, experiences of violence and its representation in the media. The data from interviews with young people suggests that opinions on this matter are varied. Some young people consider that, because most people can distinguish between fact and fantasy, violence on film and television is harmless and even fun. Others feel that such violence can influence the behaviour of young children and some young people in a negative way. The main theme identified from the interviews is that people can distinguish between fact and fantasy. People can control the media, but not real encounters with violence. This may be one of the most important points raised by the interviews, especially when we relate this to one of the symptoms of PTSD — Learned Helplessness.

Chapter 4
The death of a child

A bereavement is always painful. However, many authors have argued that the death of a child is one of the most devastating events that a family can endure (Lundin, 1984; Miles, 1985; Anderson *et al*, 1988; Miles, 1990). This chapter discusses the effects that the death of a child can have on a family and community.

We begin our discussion with an exploration of how the young people interviewed for this study presented their views and feelings about the death of a young person. In this context, many also expressed ideas about funerals. This is followed by a discussion of the responses of parents and siblings to the death of a child. Laungani (1995) declares:

> *'Whether Indian or British, children are the custodians of the future. When they die the future dies with them and is buried in the past. In that sense, the death of a child is the most traumatic event of any parent's life.'*

Littlewood (1992) has argued that in contemporary western society people no longer expect children to die and when such an event occurs, it conflicts with their life-cycle expectations. Such life-cycle expectations include assumptions that death is something that happens only when we grow old. In contemporary western society, such assumptions are understandable given that child mortality rates have fallen steadily during the last century, due to improvements in our knowledge of health issues and wider social and environmental improvements. However, despite these improvements, children still die from a number of causes. These include: cancer, chronic and acute childhood illnesses, accidents and suicides (Miles, 1985).

The expectation that children will no longer die, may have contributed to the current lack of adequate support for bereaved parents, siblings and friends of the dead child. Concern about this lack of support has been the impetus behind the development of bereavement support groups and death education programs, as discussed in the concluding chapter. In recent years, there has been an increasing development of such initiatives, which have grown parallel to professional bereavement support. Growth in both areas has been partly influenced by the assumption that the informal support systems, once existing in the communities and extended families of the past, are now disappearing. As discussed in *Chapter 1*, and further in this chapter, a number of factors shape the patterns of bereavement support available in a community, and it is wrong to make sweeping general-isations and assumptions.

It is important not to develop a cynical or dismissive attitude about the value of professional support, particularly one based on the premise that the old ways were 'better'. Support systems of the older communities of Bolton, generally appear to have been effective. These practices were developed and based on experience, tradition and historical conditions. The traditional view in the north has been that funeral attendance was very important. The funeral was a means of displaying respect for the deceased as well as an opportunity to grieve. However, the effectiveness of such traditions for bereaved individuals represents issues that need to be researched if they are to inform practice. It is wrong to dismiss experience as a source of learning. It is equally wrong to assume that experience always leads to learning or that experiential knowledge is always better than other ways of knowing.[1]

Stewart and Dent (1994) consider that the role of the professionals is to support bereaved parents so that they can continue to be good parents to surviving children. Wells (1990) notes that bereaved parents are not always the best people to support surviving children because they are often over-whelmed by grief. The problem with this view is that it provides a very limited and functional concept of the support professionals can give to bereaved families. It does not suggest concern for the needs of parents who lose an only child and does not allow scope for the development of systems of support for bereaved children, such as siblings or peers of the dead or

---

1   Theoretical knowledge is of equal importance.

dying child. The impact that the death of a child has on the parents is discussed later in this chapter. Due to lack of access to bereaved parents, no interview material is available for this part of the discussion, so instead, secondary sources have been drawn on. The discussion begins with an exploration of young people's experiences and perceptions of the death of a child.

The stages of grief, ie. anger, denial, shock and numbness, which are discussed in the introductory chapter, are fairly general responses in most cases of bereavement. Responses to bereavement are also shaped by the nature of the loss and the circumstances in which it occurs. When considering such matters, account must be taken of the subjective experience of grief, which is purely individual, and the long-term social and sometimes economic consequences, which are mainly cultural. In Indian society, for example, the death of a son will have greater significance and impact on the family than the death of a daughter. This is because, in India, a son is a greater financial asset to a family than a daughter because of strong cultural expectations that he will provide for his parents once they grow old. Conformity with ancient Hindu scriptures also demands that only sons may light the funeral pyre and perform the last funeral rites for their parents (Laungani, 1995). This does not mean that Indian families love sons more or less than they love a daughter, nor does it imply that the pain, grief and intensity experience by bereaved Indian parents is any different if they lose a son rather than a daughter. It simply means that in India, in social economic terms, the death of a son has more impact on a family. Although this is due to cultural rather than individual concerns, culture does have long-term consequences for individuals. This is why the systems of support available within a community are so important, as are the values it shares.

It seems so obvious to say that the death of a child can have a devastating impact on the family as a whole. Each member of a bereaved family is an individual who needs to grieve in his or her own way. Thus, for people who are experiencing grief, the presence of others who also need support, but who may be grieving differently means that bereaved members of a family can have a negative and even destructive influence on each other (Miles, 1990).

The death of a member of a community has an impact on those outside the family as well. In a community organised around relational principles, the impact may be very hard, particularly when a child dies. Within the family, the death of a child is a blow to the bereaved patents and surviving siblings. In the community, the death of a child is felt by all other parents in that community. This is not to argue that other parents feel a loss similar in intensity to that of the bereaved parents. However, as the death of someone of our own age brings home our own mortality, the death of a child forces us to acknowledge our children's mortality. The death of any child symbolises the potential death of all our children and, as such, is grieved and feared by all. The death also has an impact on the child's peers. This is why close knit communities can be so helpful. In such communities, friends and neighbours provide the emotional and practical support that is so necessary when families experience the death of a child. The importance of such community support is illustrated by a woman interviewed by Anderson *et al* (1988) who discusses her experience of grief and isolation after the death of her daughter. The bereavement was far more difficult for her than it might have been because, shortly after her daughter's death, her husband found work in London and she had to move away from her local community:

> *"I think that I cried for most of the time, for my husband was on night work, and I amongst strangers and thinking of my poor child who I had so recently buried.'*

(Anderson *et al,* 1988)

Exploring the ways in which communities that are structured around relational principles can provide support to bereaved families, has been the main aim of this study. The purpose of the first section of this chapter is to relate some of the interview material to consideration of how a child's death can have an impact on young people in the community. The main theme to emerge from the interviews was the importance, not just of the funeral, but also of the way this was conducted. As discussed in previous chapters, not all the people interviewed considered that it was a good thing for children to attend funerals. Indeed, the young adult man cited below had quite adamant views about this:

"No, I don't think that it's a good idea, children going to funerals, I think funerals are a bad idea altogether. It's just more grief, I mean those services, they are so depressing. I suppose it does put you in touch with your emotions, or so they say. But, well how helpful is that? And how much has that got to do with the grief you really feel for the person who died? I mean, lets face it, you can come away from the funeral of someone you hardly knew and feel depressed — well how real is that? I think it's the way it's done really, the service, I mean, it's so depressing. I really don't think it helps people, especially not children get over things, I honestly don't. I think it makes it worse ... I think it's morbid. But then, it's really the way it's done, like I say, I mean, I watched a program on telly once of a black person's funeral. Now to me that is how a funeral could help, the way they were doing it on that program. Because they did it like a celebration, like they were having a party. And they were all singing and dancing and talking about the person who died, but it was a happy event, you know, now to me that is much more helpful. But the like, standard church funeral, with that boring service, and its like, some of the things that are said, just have absolutely nothing at all to do with the person who died. I mean, its torture it's so boring, I mean, everyone is looking at their watch half way through and wishing it was through — what has that to do with real mourning? Usually its just boring but it can be quite a bad thing, its just morbid, morbid and depressing. and I definitely don't think that children should be subjected to it."

A funeral one of the authors attended, which explicitly took the form of a celebration and a tribute, was that of a late colleague. She found it a very moving experience. A life can be celebrated in many ways and not just as part of the formal funeral service. There have been other celebrations of a life in Bolton and these have included the celebration of the life of a child. Memorials have been held in public places, such as one of the local parks. Memories have been shared, favourite songs of the deceased have been sung by friends and played by high fidelity systems. Flowers have been laid on the ground and candles lit. Sometimes friends and relatives and, indeed, children have made contributions to the funeral services, in the form of public reminiscence and tributes to the deceased. Over the years, the communities of Halliwell and Astley Bridge have witnessed bereavements caused by the deaths of young children and people, as well as adults and older people. What is most significant when such tragedies have occurred, is the selflessness of bereaved parents who have shown a willingness to involve other children and their families in the funerals and other memorial services. Typically these take the form of a celebration of the life of the deceased and churches now appear to encourage participation of relatives and friends of the deceased in their services. The general trend is for funeral services to become more the celebration of a life, rather than the mourning of a death.

The theme of celebration predominated in most of the interviews conducted for this study. There was a difference in the ways older and younger people referred to celebration, with older people being more indirect in their interpretation. But such differences appeared to be a choice of words rather than meaning. The Irish wake, for example, is one traditional funeral that is based on the theme of celebration, although the author has never heard it referred to specifically as such. The implicit theme of the notion of celebration also came up on some nineteenth century mourning cards inspected during the course of the research. These form part of the archive collection in the local studies section of Bolton Central Library:

> *In Remembrance of James Lawson. Who died September 27th, 1858 and was interred at the Bolton Cemetery in September 30th. In the 23rd year of his age.*
>
> *None who had the pleasure of his acquaintance will refuse the tribute of a tear to his memory. As a son, he was dutiful, obedient and kind, as a brother, anxious ever for the happiness of the family circle, and with no ambition beyond that of acquiring a character for moral excellence and unassuming piety. As a friend, he was warmhearted, sincere and sympathising, and, what is perhaps a rare*

feature of life, he never made any enemies. He had just completed his studies at Battersea College, and gave promise of a brilliant career, when death, who spares neither young nor old, placed upon him his icy hand, and cut him off in the very hour looked forward to by his parents, relatives and friends as that in which his studies being terminated, the active duties of life for which he was qualified would be hopefully commenced. May he rest in peace.

The example above — linking the concept of celebration to the data collected — contains many of the components that constitute a celebration. There is balance in the reminiscence. There is an acknowledgment for the joy of life and the tragedy of death. The narrative rejoices for the achievements of a life that has been lived and pays tribute to these. But there is also a sense of loss for all the wasted potential of that life due to the young man's early death. The difference in this narrative from the approach to grieving discussed by the young people interviewed, is the acknowledgement that death comes to old and young. As one of the young men interviewed put it:

"When I die, I don't want people to be upset, I want them to be happy for the life I have had. I mean, it is sad when someone dies, but it does come to us all. And to me the most important thing to think about, no matter how old someone is when they die, is, how happy was the life that they had. Me, I've had a good life so far, its been a happy life and with a bit of luck it will carry on being happy. To me, its not so much dying, you know what I'm trying to say, its the having a life in the first place that's important like. Having had the opportunity you know what I mean, just to have lived. No matter how long or short it is, its the having lived that's important. So it is sad when someone dies, for you because you will miss them and that really hurts, I mean, it can be really unbearable. You feel it like, inside. But as far as I'm concerned, I don't want people to be sad for me, because I'll be OK. Well what I mean by that is, if I'm dead, well let's face it, no one and nothing can ever hurt me."

Another young person felt that tributes paid to the deceased during a funeral should focus more on the person's positive, humanistic qualities, and what these have helped him/her to achieve, rather than status or materialistic achievements. This belief related to the young man's belief in reincarnation, a popular theme that came up during the interviews with young people. The young man concerned expressed himself with such eloquence that we have included below, quite a large section of his transcript.

"See I don't see the point really in bringing up that such and such a body, them who have died, was President of this or that; or had achieved a lot as far as brain learning goes. That might be a help as far as what that achievement did for others, like, the knock on effect. But that is, sort of academic or career learning and I don't think that it's what you take with you. Lets face it, you have two sorts of yous really, and they both have a capacity for learning. Like, the brain, that can absorb a lot of learning in this life and that learning is essential for the place you will be sort of filling here. So the brain can take in lots of information, like literature and learning that you do at school, or university or in your job. But after you die, there is very little of that which you will need in your next life. I mean the world is changing. What you learned in a life you lived say, two hundred years ago won't be that much use if you come back now.

So I think that the amount of learning our brains can take in is quite limited, limited that is when we compare it to the soul. Now the soul that's the bit we take with us. I believe that the learning of the soul, well I think there is no limit to it really. And the learning of the soul, that is the enduring part, the learning that lasts and we need in all our lives. Things like imagination; I mean, imagination, creativity, there are no limits to that. I really believe that there are absolutely no limits to peoples' creativity or imagination. And the soul, well, the brain is only so big, it's like a container if you see what I mean, it will only take so much. But like your soul, it has no boundaries because it's not a physical thing, its like mythical, you know.

Qualities like, the ability to make people believe, like, to inspire them. Kindness, the ability to share, the courage to do things like fight for what you believe in. To me these are the qualities we need to remember when a person dies; because these are the qualities they will be taking with them. Of course there are the bad qualities as well and unfortunately I think we take those with us as well. Cruelty, sneakiness, snideness, jealousy. Suppose it wouldn't be nice to dwell on them too much, but in moderation they're not bad. Some people live all their lives and never develop the good things, and I think it's a shame when people die and those who are left can only think about those. Do you know, in some ways being out of work can help in that. When you have a job you are too busy to think. Being unemployed can give you time to think, but not always about the good things I know. Maybe that's why a lot of older people when they retire go like, well they sort of calm down don't they, go milder? They have time to realise that it's those enduring things that matter. Some never do though, they are the ones that get 'nowt' as they get older because they can only value the material things and like, status. It crazy when you think about it. I mean, in a hundred years from now, who will give a shit if you were like, the boss of this or that now. And it's sad because they can live not just one life but many lives and still not learn. To me, that's in a way, yes it's sad when a young person dies.

But who knows, maybe their times came sooner to move on to a better state because they learned those qualities quicker. I believe that all life has purpose, and the main purpose is developing those better qualities so that we can move on to a better state. If you get those qualities quite young, well in a way there's not much point hanging around here is there? Might as well move on. See people say when a young person dies, all that wasted potential — but maybe they did reach their potential. Maybe that's why they died in the first place."[2]

---

2   This young man was aged 23 years at the time of his interview in 1996.

Indirectly the young person quoted above is acknowledging his observation that adults who reach mid life begin to reflect on and revisit issues they explored in youth. *Chapter 2* explained that this phenomenon is referred to by some writers as 'middlescence'. The interesting thing to note about the young man's narrative is that he talks a lot about human potential. But he uses the word 'potential' in a very different way to that in which many people have now learned to interpret it. In this century we have come to value theoretical[3] knowledge, personal promotion, success and power. This western individualism has reached its peak in the last few years with the promotion of an 'I'm all right Jack' mentality, in which self-interest and selfishness are considered admirable human strengths. Yet the young man uses 'potential' as a way of describing a kind of personal growth in which tolerance and respect for others become the priority. Note that he makes frequent reference to the fact that, when someone dies, it is the impact that the deceased had on other people's lives that is remembered. If these are the qualities remembered, perhaps they are, as the young man claims, the most important qualities to which we should aspire. The young man also gives an interesting perspective on the death of a young person because we often think of this as a waste. Yet the young man considers the possibility that 'maybe their times come sooner to move on to a better state because they learned those qualities quicker.' The young man also offers an alternative view on unemployment, pointing out that this can give a person the time and space to reflect. Although this view may not be popular, it forms a basis for reflection. Another young person expressed a wish that, in the event of his death, people would remember not only how he lived his present life, but his aspirations for the next one:

> *"Like me, if I get my own way in the next life, I'll come back as a bird of prey or a tiger. I think that both tigers*

---

3   While not wishing to challenge the validity of the young man's testimony, we note that theoretical knowledge can be used to attain the very qualities he values. Theoretical knowledge can be used in many ways, personal growth is one of them.

and birds of prey are beautiful and there is so much about them you can admire, their freedom, their independence. They are brave as well, they are afraid of nothing. They don't have to fear anyone putting them down, they don't have to hide because they have no fear. They don't have to worry about anything, just live day to day. Its interesting actually, but ever since I was a little kid I've loved tigers. But I found out last year that according to the Chinese Horoscope, my sign is the tiger, you know, I am a tiger. So who knows, maybe I'll really be one in my next life. So, I don't want people to be upset when I die, because with a bit of luck I'll be a tiger, or a bird of prey flying over their heads."[4]

Another common theme to arise during the interviews was the importance of funerals as a way in which to share grief. Again, younger people were more likely to discuss this openly, as shown below:

"I think that funerals are good because you are all together and sharing it, the grief and all that, with everyone else and helping each other to deal with it. So you don't feel that you are alone when you feel sad, because you do feel dead sad when someone you know, especially someone of your own age, dies. But it definitely helps to know that everyone else, your mates and all that feel the same. And it gives you an opportunity to talk about it and get it all out. You know, it's that sharing it that is important." [5]

As this young man made his concluding comments, he held out his arms in front of his chest, symbolically putting his arms around someone. The significance of this gesture to the author, was the quite unconscious way it was done. It suggested that when he has attended a funeral, the sharing of comfort stemming from physical contact has been part of his experience and is now his expectation. Dyregrow and Kingsley (1991) have found that the surviving children of bereaved

---

4   Young man aged 19 years at the time of his interview in 1996.
5   As above.

parents, can experience terrible feelings of social isolation if they do not have an opportunity to share their grief with friends. If surviving siblings are denied the opportunity to witness people of their own age crying and expressing emotion because of a bereavement, they may feel that such expressions of emotion are unacceptable to the peer group. This may inhibit them from expressing their emotions when they are with friends. Stewert and Dent (1994) assert that young children need to be able to give comfort as well as receive it.

Talking with others about the deceased was another important theme to emerge from the data. In many respects, talking about the deceased is another form of celebration, which has been part of traditional practice during the Irish wake. But talking is also useful because it provides an opportunity to name emotions and to talk through the experience of grief. Kiztinger and Kiztinger (1989) consider that a vital part of coming to terms with grief is acknowledging it, talking about it and giving the feelings experienced a name. In *Chapter 2* we discussed how a young child's limited language skills can make it difficult for him/her to name what he or she is experiencing. Sharing with others can create an opportunity for younger children to overcome such a handicap. Funerals also give younger children the opportunity to learn the kinds of feelings they can expect to feel when they suffer a bereavement.

The young person cited above goes on to discuss what for him, is the social significance of attendance at a funeral:

"If someone dies that you care about and you don't go to the funeral, then you're not showing that person respect."

The data from the interviews conducted for this study and work by other authors, suggest that this is very much the traditional view in the north west of England. A good 'turn out' at a funeral is considered to be important because it symbolises respect for the deceased. This symbol of respect benefits the bereaved in that it can provide comfort. Conformity with such practice also means that a larger group of people will be available to talk about the deceased. At a funeral gathering, people talk about the deceased in a very special way, as a person they had known, so that the latter's name will be mentioned several times during the funeral conversations. This reminds us of discussions in *Chapter 1*, of how speech can be a way of bringing about the presence of a kind of tangible essence of the deceased. Reverend A Miles (1990) reports that in his experience many bereaved parents find it very comforting when they hear others refer to their dead child by name. To all who have contact with a bereaved family, ie. friends, teachers or health care practitioners, he stresses the importance of naming the deceased, rather than using nameless identification such as 'it' or 'your child'.

One difference that did emerge between the accounts given by the older interviewees and those given by the younger people were the attitudes towards viewing the body of the deceased. In Kenny *et al* (1998a) the symbolic social and therapeutic practice of laying-out and paying the last respects to the deceased by viewing the body was discussed. In *Chapter 1* some discussion was devoted to young people's attitudes towards viewing the body and it appears that from the data collected, this practice is undergoing a gradual demise. One of the younger people interviewed had experienced viewing the body of a young person who had died. Others had viewed the body of an older person. The person cited below was unsure about the value of such practice:

"*A couple of years ago a friend of mine died, he was slightly younger than me. Anyway, he was really popular and well liked and to be honest, his death . . . Well it knocked the lot of us for six really. Anyway, his mum was really good about it, I think she could understand the effect it had on all of us like, younger people. She invited his (the deceased) friends to pay their last respects if they wanted to do and quite a lot went with their parents and that. I couldn't make my mind up what to do, I still don't know if I did the right thing by not going. In the end I didn't go. But every one of my mates that did go said that they found it really useful, you know, they felt a lot better afterwards. He looked really peaceful they said.*"

Throughout the research for this book, the theme of the selflessness of bereaved parents has come up time and time again. The mother described above was no doubt suffering a deep and profound sense of grief. But despite this, she still had time to consider the feelings of her late son's friends. She cared enough to allow them a last opportunity to say good-bye. Evidence from the extract above and from the literature suggests that such an invitation would have been very comforting and helpful for those who chose to take it. Several writers have noted that viewing the body of the deceased can be helpful for a variety of reasons. Mostly, they consider that it helps to accept the loss. Dyregrow and Kingsley (1991) consider it helpful for siblings of a dead child to see the deceased. In the case of a baby or small child, they may also find it useful to give him or her a last cuddle if they wish. If this is conducted in the presence of the parents and other family members, it can help bereaved siblings to feel included. This can protect children from developing feelings of isolation. Midwives and other health care professionals are becoming more sensitive to the needs of bereaved families and are responding in very innovative ways, for example, by having a family photograph taken when a baby dies. Although such practices can be useful, it is always important to remember individual differences and to respect the principle of choice. Note, for example, that the mother referred to above, gave the young people of her community an invitation and not an instruction, to pay their last respects to her son. A hospital relatives' liaison officer and a forensic pathologist interviewed considered that there is sometimes a danger that parents can be pressured into seeing and handling their dead child, by well-meaning professionals, when this is not really what they want. In relation to the death of a baby, or a still birth, the pathologist made the following points:

"Then they (health care professionals) are shoving the baby into the mother's arms and saying 'you must nurse the baby.' Now I have had a lot of feedback from that, and what I'm finding is that not a lot of mothers want to do that there and then. And some have said, 'I've suffered because of it.' Because the baby wasn't washed, it wasn't dressed, it's not whatever. They come down here sometimes afterwards, and by this time, we have had time to wash and dress the little baby, you know? We can maybe get a little doll and use its small clothes and put it on, you know? And they feel a lot better afterwards. I'm not saying they are all like that. Some mothers do want to

hold their babies. But the point I'm making is that it's wrong to automatically assume that they all do."

From the data collected for this study, it appears to have been the practice for bereaved parents in Bolton to invite peers to pay their last respects. However, the accounts given by the older individuals were different, in that such invitations in the recent past would take place in the home. One of the older persons interviewed recalled that:

"A friend of mine, a young lad had died, and they had the coffin in the front room. The day he was buried, his mum came to the door. We were all playing in the front street, and asked us if we wanted to pay our last respects. I can remember seeing him in his tiny coffin and not being at all afraid. His family was one of the poorest in the street, his mum had about six kids. I can remember, I was very young, and I watched her (the mother) seeing to the other children as bravely as she could. And as young as I was (I'd be about seven) I knew that her heart was absolutely breaking." [6]

The person cited above recalls that at the time the event described took place she was a small child and yet she was still able to recognise the mother's distress. If this distress could be recognised by a child, this implies that it was also recognised by other adult members of the family and community. It may have been comforting for the mother that her child had died at home and that she was sharing the reminiscences of his friends during the funeral. But additional and more long-term sources of support may have been there, because the young boy died at home, in the context of the community. So the funeral described by the older person may have been situated in the centre of a continuum of care and support, prior to and after the death. There is good reason to speculate that this may well have been the case because both Halliwell and Astley Bridge have always been very 'neighbourly' areas. Although the woman interviewed did not go on to discuss what happened to the bereaved family after the funeral, it could be

---

6   This woman was aged 60 years at the time of her interview in 1994.

assumed (with some caution) that friends, neighbours and family may well have 'popped' into the house to continue providing emotional and, indeed, practical support, for several weeks or even months after the funeral.

Had the woman's child died in a hospital environment, then the situation may have been very different. Miles (1985) has reported that in his experience, when a child dies in hospital, the bereaved parents can find it very difficult to leave. Indeed, some may stay for hours until they are escorted to the door. For many parents, the main (and possibly only) source of support when they lose a child, may be the hospital staff who cared for him or her. Under such circumstances, leaving the hospital symbolises not only their last source of contact with their dead child, but also, the severing of links with people who have helped and supported them. This is especially the case, if the child had been ill for many weeks or months prior to the death.

Kubler-Ross (1983) reports that some dying children like to plan their own funerals and often enjoy the involvement of siblings and school friends in these arrangements. In her book, Kubler-Ross gives the case example of the sister of a terminally ill boy, who planned her brother's funeral with help from her classmates. The girl's mother was a single parent who had nursed her son throughout his long illness, with very little support from anyone. So she was feeling both grieved and exhausted when her son died. This incentive on the part of the dead boy's sibling and friends proved to be beneficial to all concerned. Kubler-Ross further reports that children who attend the funeral of a dead friend can gain comfort in a variety of other ways. Little gestures like placing small personal possessions in the coffin and singing school songs can all be helpful. The most comforting experience of all for most children, is that of just simply being there at the funeral and reminiscing about the dead child with friends.

Although several of the people interviewed for this study had attended funerals and some had experienced paying their last respects, no-one had any experience of having made contributions to the planning or presentations of these. The author has known children to make contributions such as those described by Kubler-Ross. It seems from the literature that in many cultures, children play an important role in funeral rituals. Kitzinger and Kitzinger cite the example of the Edo in Nigeria, a society in which children play a key role in the funeral rites when an adult dies. In this society, the funeral rituals last six days. On the sixth day a child is chosen to represent the dead person. The other children of the community dance with him, while he explains that they must be good from now on and that he will not be able to take care of them in future.

Parkes (1972) writes that grief is the price we pay for love. The bereaved and the dead they mourn once had a caring and frequently loving relationship, but which was rarely what we might call perfect. Because of this people can be contradictory when they talk about death. In the interviews with young people, the author found that, while interviewees recognised the importance of expressing, sharing and experiencing grief, they also expressed a wish that in the event of their own death, they did not want their families and friends to grieve for them. This was partly due to the common theme found in the interviews, discussed in *Chapters 1* and *2*. Most of the young people interviewed expressed a love of life, and of living for the moment, rather than too much concern with death. However, they did not want to be responsible for causing the suffering of those they love. When we die, whether we like it or not, we are the cause of our loved one's pain and suffering. This is a responsibility that some of the young people interviewed did acknowledge but felt very uncomfortable with:

> *"For my personal self I'm not afraid of dying, I mean, I'd rather live than die obviously, but I'm not afraid of it. But the thing that really worries me about dying is that I will hurt the people that I love. For me that's the main worry about my personal death, those I'll leave behind and the fact that I'll be hurting them."*[7]

Another young woman added:

---

7   Young man aged 20 years at the time of his interview in 1996.

"Yes, I agree with that. In fact, I think that if someone told me I was going to die, I think that for me my first worry would be, how do I tell my family. For me anyway, the thoughts of having to face them and tell them and to see them upset, that to me... well it can't bear thinking about really. It would really hurt me, far more than knowing that I was going to die.'

Kubler-Ross (1983) argues that parents of a terminally ill child should share their grief with the child. This is because it provides an opportunity for the child to be told much he/she is loved. It is also an opportunity for the parents and their child to grieve together. The young people when interviewed were discussing their hypothetical death. But it may be the case that any distress which would arise if such a hypothetical situation became real, could be shared. This is because, Kubler-Ross (1969) has found that many people who have a terminal illness feel a need to mourn their own death. Another advantage with terminally ill young people being aware of the fact that they are going to die, is that they can share with others, not only coming to terms with this, but also the planning of their own funeral. This planning, after the death, provides further material for reminiscence at the funeral and we will come back to this discussion later in the chapter. The point made by the young people that they would not want their relatives to be sad if they died provides further support for the theme of celebration. A celebration can encompass many emotions, including happiness and sadness. There is evidence to suggest that both laughter and tears have an equally important role when it comes to dealing with stressful situations, such as that caused by a bereavement (Kenny, 1998a). When we consider funeral practices, perhaps there is an argument for organising them so that they enable the expression of a wide range of emotions, not just sadness.

Finally it seems that, on the basis of the interviews conducted for this study, when a child dies funeral attendance can be a very useful form of support for the young friends of the deceased. This is due to a number of reasons. For example, a funeral provides an opportunity to share grief with others, to talk and to reminisce. The way in which the funeral is organised was also found to be important. Funerals organised around the theme of a celebration appear to offer the most support to the bereaved.

However, we have to be careful not to assume that the funeral provides all the support that a bereaved person or persons require. Once the funeral is over, follow-up support for the bereaved may be lacking. Once the collective sense of mourning and support provided by the funeral has passed, there is a danger that the bereaved may be neglected. It is during the weeks following a funeral that professional help may be needed. If there is a failure to provide this, the bereaved can begin to feel isolation and despair. In the following section, the effects of a bereavement on parents are discussed, together with some of the factors that can either help or hinder the giving of help and support.

Bereaved parents were not interviewed for this study, discussion being based mainly on literature reviews. Interview data in which people have referred to their experience of coming into contact with bereaved parents is also used. The issues covered come under the broad heading of feelings of guilt. Also explored are some of the factors that can influence such feelings. Gender and how gender stereotyping and socialisation can mitigate against bereaved fathers working through the tasks of grief are included, and we conclude the chapter with some discussion of how the allocation of meaning can play an important role in coming to terms with the death of a child, and how parents can achieve this aim.

Feelings of guilt

Thanatologists who have worked with bereaved parents have reported that the most difficult emotions for the latter to cope with are feelings of guilt. Kubler-Ross, who has had a great deal of experience of working with bereaved parents, argues that this guilt is usually unnecessary. Guilt can stem from parents blaming themselves in some way for the child's death, a feeling that they could have prevented it. But Kubler-Ross (1983) states that, in reality, this is rarely the case. In the case of death caused by sudden or infectious illness, a child's condition usually deteriorates very quickly. In such circumstances it is understandable if parents or caregivers do not recognise the symptoms in sufficient time for something to be done. In the case of accidental death, in order to ensure that a child never suffers an accident, we would have to wrap them up in cotton wool. One has to ask in such a circumstance, what quality of life would such a child have? Kubler-Ross also asks bereaved parents to consider would their dead child want them to torment themselves in this way. The answer is — probably not. In relation to the data collected for this book, we draw attention to some of the interviews we conducted with young people. Many of these young people expressed a wish that, in the event of their deaths, they would not want the people they love to suffer unduly. Others pointed out that if they were to discover that they had a terminal illness, then the most difficult thing for them would be the task of telling their families. This was because they were very concerned that the people they love should not suffer because of them. Nevertheless, despite these rationales, people of all ages experience guilt for a whole range of reasons when they suffer a bereavement (recall the young woman cited in *Chapter 2* who suffered guilty feelings because she wanted to thank her late father for a cream egg he had given her).

   Miles (1995) has identified three sources of potential guilt, which she defined as cultural role guilt, moral guilt and survival guilt. Cultural role guilt stems from the parents' perception that they have failed in their responsibilities because they could not prevent the death of their child. Moral guilt is caused by their perception that the child's death is a punishment for some passed sin. Survival guilt comes when parents feel that it is wrong for them to have survived their child. Many parents who lost an adult child during the First and Second World Wars suffered survival guilt and parents who experience such guilt express this by seeking some meaning which will explain their child's death. It was this need to find meaning that led to the growth of an interest in spiritualism after the Great War. One of the women interviewed for this study was quite convinced that the death of an older woman she had known, was hastened because of the death of an adult son:

*"I always put it down to that (the son's death). I mean I
know she was a good age, but she really went downhill
after that, she really did. She kept saying, it's not right, a
mother shouldn't outlive her own son, and she really
went downhill after that."*[8]

Moral guilt presents a similar problem to that of transductive
thinking, discussed in *Chapter 2*. Something the parents said
or did prior to the death of the child can intensify such
feelings. An example of this is provided by one of the women
who took part in a study conducted by Anderson and Zinsser
(1988). In the citation below the woman describes the death of
her second daughter who died of croup:

*"Six weeks before this (the child becoming ill) she had
done something wrong. I beat her and told her that the
bad man would have her, and when she was dying she
said, 'you beat me and told me that the bad man would
have me. Is he going to have me now?' Just imagine my
feelings when I said to her 'no, he will not have you.'"*

(cited in Anderson *et al*, 1988)

Cultural role guilt can lead parents to tormenting themselves
with 'if onlys'. 'If only I had loved him or her more.' One of the
cruellest blows death brings, is the knowledge that there is no,
'once more' no second chance. Yet when we lose someone we
love, we would give so much, just for that 'one more time'. 'If
only I could hold him or her, one more time.' 'If only I could
hear his/her voice, just one more time.' But there are no
second chances. And even if we had a second, third or
thousandth 'one more time' this would never take away the
pain of loss, nor compensate for it. It is the very taken-
for-granted presence of those we love that is the source of
spontaneity in relationships, and spontaneity is about sharing
a moment. No matter how many moments we have shared
with the people we love, once we lose them, life will continue
presenting us with moments. And many of these will be
moments we would enjoy so much more if only we could share

8   This woman was aged 86 years at the time of her interview in 1992.

them with the person we have loved and lost. We can only appreciate presence when there is absence. Our shared experiences with those we love stem not just from the presence of that person, but the context in which we share these experiences. Cultural role guilt can lead to some parents trying to protect the dead child in some way. This serves as a form of compensation for the ways in which they believe that they failed to care for them in life. Miles writes of a mother who made a coverlet of flowers for her daughter's grave to protect her against the snow. This may be why so many of the people interviewed for this study, both young and old, spoke of the importance of talking about the deceased. It seems that this 'speaking into being' is of real therapeutic value to the bereaved. It appears to be a way of hanging on, which is necessary and therefore, not pathological.

Feelings of anger are common following a bereavement, but these can be complicated by guilt. Bereaved parents may try to cope with feelings of guilt and anger by transferring their feelings onto the other partner. Each partner may blame the other for failing the deceased child. There is also a risk that bereaved parents may feel impatient with surviving siblings because they believe that they are not grieving appropriately. Miles writes that one parent or relative may deny him/herself the opportunity to work through the tasks of grief because he/she is trying to remain strong for others. There is evidence in the story cited on *Page 97* about the little boy who had died, that this might have happened to the mother described in the scenario. When we consider the end of the story, the woman interviewed recalls that:

> "I watched her (the mother) seeing to the other children as bravely as she could . . . and as young as I was, I'd be about seven, I knew that her heart was absolutely breaking."

In this case, it appears to have been the mother who felt the need to be strong, although Miles writes that, in general, it is men or grandparents who adopt this position. This situation may be more likely to develop if there is no outside support available to the family. It is difficult to know from the interview, how the mother described fared long-term. There was no mention during the interview of any specific person who may have been available to help. However, the interviewee did go on to discuss neighbourly support in Bolton following a bereavement. Drawing on this, other information given by the older women interviewed and, in addition, the work of Roberts (1989) some inferences can be made. For example, the role of the layer-out, who at the time the woman based her story were still quite active in Bolton, was quite important during a funeral and for some weeks afterwards. This is because of the unobtrusive yet supportive manner in which they helped with the organisation and practicalities of the funeral. The value of such an approach has been discussed in some detail by Wells (*op cit*).

Funerals can serve as a source of social support and comfort. Despite this, symptoms of bereavement, such as shock and numbness, can make it difficult for the bereaved to make decisions or deal with the practicalities of organising the funeral. Miles writes that it is not uncommon to hear the bereaved saying things like 'I don't know what to do' or 'what do I do next'. Helpers who provide long-term support for bereaved people come from many backgrounds. Such helpers may be friends of the bereaved, members of the family or professionals who have been involved in the care of the deceased prior to the death. In funerals in the north west of England, and particularly in Bolton, neighbours and/or the layer-out, would often call on the family for a few days after the funeral, to see how the parents were coping (Roberts, 1989; Kenny, 1998a). Research suggests that such practice can be a great source of comfort to some people, but is not necessarily welcomed by everyone. The practice of a follow-up visit, in itself, may not be enough. The attitude and approach adopted by the helper is also important.

Miles (1990) recommends that before visiting bereaved parents, helpers should first establish whether or not this is welcome. If bereaved parents do want a follow-up visit, then helpers should ensure that they have a reasonable amount of time to spare, ie. approximately an hour, before making the visit. Otherwise, they can give the impression that they are paying a 'duty visit'. Indeed, before any helper pays such a visit he/she should question his/her motives for doing so. Is it a duty visit? If this is the motivation, it is probably advisable not to visit. If the visitor is genuinely concerned, when he/she arrives at the home of the bereaved, he/she will need to find ways to demonstrate his/her sincerity. Miles advises that helpers, once they enter the house, immediately remove any outside clothing they might be wearing. If a helper calling on a bereaved family appears in a rush, this can be interpreted as a 'duty visit.' If a helper really has no time to visit bereaved parents, Miles suggests that sending a card or note, or making a telephone call can be just as beneficial and may, in some cases, be less intrusive.

If there is little support outside the family, this may increase the risk of one partner adopting a strong supportive role. Miles writes that, in her experience, it is generally grandparents and fathers who assume that they have a duty to adopt this role. She writes:

> *'Recently, after telling a couple and the maternal grandmother that their newborn infant was not going to live, the two women sobbed and talked about their pain. The father sat off to the side looking sad, but saying nothing. Finally, the grandmother said, "he has to be strong for both of us". I intervened at this point and said, "perhaps, but I know that fathers have lots of tears and many sad feelings too. It's OK if he isn't strong for you, you can all grieve together". At this point, tears came into the father's eyes and his wife reached out to him.'*

This assumption that fathers should be the strong, supportive partner when a child dies appears to be quite common and it was an issue raised by some of the people interviewed. Two health care professionals cited below, challenged this stereotyping. The first, a man, drew on his own experience:

Respondent 1: *"But from the male point of view, if you see a cot death baby, well I can remember when mine was babies. I mean, my oldest one is 18 years old now. But I can remember her when she was really tiny, and like, 16 months old and all this. And I have sat out there, and I've sat and cried with the mothers and fathers who have lost their babies. Cried with them because it was the only way that I could to get rid of all*

> *the emotion in me. Like I say, I am a father, so*
> *I can say that I can see it from the father's*
> *point of view. "*

Respondent 2: *"Yes, because the fathers get pushed out don't*
they?"

Respondent 1: *"Yes, I've seen a lot of it, you know where the*
father has been pushed to one side. And people
tend to forget that it is his child too, you know,
he has suffered a loss. And I think that tends to
get neglected. " [9]

There appears to be a strong social pressure for men to adopt a supportive role. But to what extent is this attitude compounded by men and society's practice of sex role stereotyping? Adopting this role may protect people from confronting the deep and painful feelings of grief. For a man socialised to believe the 'men don't cry' ideology, it may be difficult to cope with painful emotions that can erode such a machismo veneer. Following bereavement, the emotions experienced are very painful and people often do what they can to avoid facing them. In the long-term, such avoidance can be damaging and the effects that adoption of this role can have on bereaved fathers needs to be considered. How concepts of masculinity can mitigate against men working through the tasks of grief should also be considered. Generally, the motivation to keep feelings under control is due to social pressure, although individuals can also impose this control on themselves. It must be acknowledged that women, and even children, can also deny their feelings. Nevertheless, there is ample evidence to suggest that men are at greater risk. Even in cultures based on relational principles, where there is no perceived shame in people expressing all emotions, including crying, it is usually women who do the wailing when a family suffers a bereavement and men organise, make arrangements and listen to the women wailing.

---

9   Transcript material taken from an interview conducted in 1995 with a
     woman in her early thirties and a man in his mid forties.

Feminists, such as Kitzinger and Kitzinger (1989) and Gilligan (1993), consider that the process of gender role stereotyping in boys begins with social pressure to disconnect from the mother and an associated femininity. This includes the ability to feel or share emotion. Kitzinger and Kitzinger refer to this separation as the first violence men experience from society. In this sense, feminists are not necessarily talking about the real flesh and blood mother, but what the mother symbolises in our culture — warmth, love, tenderness and comfort. The concept of femininity, not necessarily referring to women, also has implicit within it, notions of dependency on others. As many writers have pointed out, this link between femininity and dependency is very simplistic and often false.

The concept and practice of dependency appears in numerous guises. If we move away from economic considerations and towards the notion of sharing feelings, this could involve depending on another person for emotional support. Women are traditionally socialised to adopt a more psychological approach based on the concept of interdependency. When women need affection, they feel less inhibited in seeking it themselves or in giving and receiving emotional support.

If we consider the symbolic mother, what is 'mothering' and what happens when we are 'mothered'? Mothering can be many things. It can include the ability to absorb another and, in this sense, can involve a 'pouring out' or an 'emptying of self' into another person. Thus 'mothering' and being 'mothered' can seem quite threating. Such absorption can lead to fears of being smothered or consumed, and we might be. But by what and by whom? The mother? Or our own feelings? The ability to allow ourselves to be mothered requires the capacity to trust, to feel and, having taken hold of our feelings, to lose them in someone else. In order to lose our feelings, we need to feel that we own them in the first place.

There is evidence in the literature to support the view that expressions of emotion, in the form of laughter and tears, are necessary for a person to accomplish the tasks of grieving (Kenny *et al*, 1998a). What is of concern is the men, and this applies to bereaved fathers in particular, who are suffering far more than they need to because they are suppressing their emotions. It could be argued that the social pressure to avoid confrontation with emotions, especially the pressure which discourages crying, is an infringement of our right to be feeling, experiencing human beings. Superficially, the loss of self which allows us to cry can be achieved quite simply. As children, some of us did it all the time with caregivers. We allowed someone to take us in their arms and hold us while we cried. Can we remember the feeling of relief, the 'lightness' of soul following such a release of emotion? But although physical contact is perhaps the most effective way of achieving 'mothering', we must also remember that there are times when such physical contact many be inappropriate or embarrassing. In such cases, this embarrassment can be a bigger burden than the emotions we wanted ease. There are other approaches to 'mothering' which are just as effective as physical contact, such as listening. But if listening is to be of help to the bereaved, it requires the concentrated attention of the listener. It has to be what professionals now refer to as 'active listening'.

The Reverend Miles recommends, when listening to members of a family who have lost a child, that the listener should refrain from sharing personal experiences of loss. The only exception to this rule would be, if the parents, knowing that the helper has experienced a similar loss, asked about this. In such a situation, Miles advises that, while it can be helpful for the listener to briefly share such an experience, he/she should not allow such sharing to shift the focus of the conversation away from the experience of the newly bereaved parents' loss to that of his/her own. Listening is a way of giving oneself to another in a spiritual rather than a physical way — and can be just as draining.

Increasingly, psychologists and workers in other disciplines are recognising the importance of listening. It has also been recognised that communication, including the communication implicit in support, has a two-way purpose. The development of listening skills is included in courses concerned with the development of communication and counselling skills. Speaking more generally about appropriate support, he also cautions against using euphemisms, such as 'passed away', and biblical, ethical or societal platitudes, such as 'you now have a little child in heaven' or 'thank God that you have other children'. However, despite offering this caution, Miles acknowledges that some parents may actually seek out spiritual or religious phrases or meanings to explain or describe their child's death.[10]

This is probably due to another characteristic of grief, the need to establish a meaning for the death of their child. This need may be very intense and parents may imagine their child as a little angel in heaven. This tendency to link a child's death with spirituality can be expressed by others outside the immediate family as the following extract from one of the interviews suggests:

"A young girl had died in the next street. And I think that she had some kind of contagious disease, diphtheria or something. So that they didn't take the coffin into the house and open it like they would normally do, they left it outside the house waiting for the funeral. And I remember, a bird came and flew, it circled all the way around the coffin. And people for weeks after, commented on this bird and the symbolism of it flying around the coffin like that."[11]

Kubler-Ross places great emphasis on the importance of spiritualism for which, she acknowledges, she has been heavily criticised. However, the extract quoted suggests that spirituality can offer comfort to some people. This need by some parents to establish a spiritual link with their child's death is illustrated in some of the verses presented below. This has been taken from a collection of popular verses that appeared on nineteenth century mourning cards. The collection of cards referred to here form part of the local history collection of Bolton Archive Library. The cards tended to be standardised postcard sized, but are varied in the degree of elaboration in the presentation. Some consist of very rich embossed paper while others are composed of plain white

---

10   The Reverend Miles *Caring for Families When a Child Dies*.
11   This woman was aged 62 years at the time of her interview in 1994.

paper with a black border. The verses also vary in their depth and elaboration from:

> *'In Affectionate Remembrance of Joseph Latham, Only Son of William and Elizabeth Melling. Who departed this life on the third instance, aged eleven years.'*

To:

> *'In Memory of Mary Jane Walker. Infant daughter of Robert and Anne Walker, who died on 28th September, aged one year and three months — interred at St. George's Church on Monday October the fourth, 1842.*
>
> *We mourn a fair and tender flower*
> *But tears alas are vain*
> *That beauteous flower*
> *Untimely nipped*
> *Shall bloom in Heaven again.'*

Many writers have noted that religious people tend to gain great comfort from their religion when they suffer a bereavement (see *References*). From this research, regardless of whether or not a person is religious and regardless of whether they believe there is something after life, establishing meaning and purpose to life appears to be the most important and helpful consideration in coming to terms with the knowledge and understanding of death and the acceptance of a bereavement. This chapter has discussed ways in which support can be provided for bereaved families and communities following the death of a child. We also revisited the funeral, this time to relate our discussion specifically to the death of a younger person. We have assessed its value as a form of social support primarily for children and young people, but also to a lesser extent for adults. The main themes to emerge from this discussion have been that it is not so much the funeral in itself that is of value but the way in which it was conducted. The most popular view shared by most interviewees was that funerals are most helpful if they take the shape of a celebration of a life rather than the mourning of a death. Funerals were also considered to be important because they provided an opportunity for people to share emotions and reminiscence of the deceased.

During the second section of the chapter we explored briefly the effects that a bereavement can have on parents. Issues, such as guilt, anger, denial of feelings and how these can be complicated were covered. Discussion has been mainly descriptive and we have offered little in the form of recommendations for practice, because we are not qualified or trained to this. What little research we have done has centred around support for children following a bereavement. We do consider support for bereaved parents to be important, but the main focus of this book has been the needs and perceptions of the child. Thus, the aim of our discussion has been to inform, at a very descriptive level, practice and research so that others may develop it further.

Chapter 5

Developing formal and informal support systems for bereaved children

During the Victorian era and following this, in the years leading up to World War One, death and dying were common topics of conversation in the family. Children were also reminded of death in stories, journals and by the death of siblings and peers (Kitzinger and Kitzinger, 1989; Dixon, 1989). However, in the years following the two wars, death became a taboo subject. The presumption grew that children needed protecting from all aspects of death and dying (Gorer, 1965). This was partly due to a belief that children did not really understand death and so did not grieve in the same way as adults, and resulted in a failure to give children appropriate support when they experienced bereavement (Stewart and Dent, 1994).

Throughout the twentieth century, children have both witnessed and suffered direct experience of several wars and conflict situations. These include the troubles in Northern Ireland, disasters such as the Bradford Stadium disaster and separations due to evacuations (Smith and Pennells, 1995). Further, the media has brought the knowledge of these events into the home. If we add to this the effects of fictional violence on television, then clearly attempts to shield children from death and dying are certain to fail.

In recent years a growing body of research has shown that separation and loss can cause children quite profound emotional and intellectual problems (Ainsworth *et al*, 1978; Bowlby, 1980). Dyregrow and Kingsley (1991) have shown that a bereaved child's education can suffer severely through difficulties in concentration and memory retention, and in feelings of alienation from their peer group. Bereavement and loss can also lead to behavioural problems (Smith and Pennells, 1995). More generally, the issues of how children are taught to confront painful and difficult situations should to be taken into account. The ability to take responsibility for dealing with such problems is part of adult life. Kitzinger and Kitzinger

(1989) argue that for adults to pretend that death does not exist implies that this is the proper way to deal with unpleasant realities in our lives and pain and suffering are better ignored.

It is becoming increasingly clear that children do need support following a loss or bereavement. The challenge facing those who support the bereaved, both formally, ie. with professional support, and informally is to find the best way to provide this. In their study, Kitzinger and Kitzinger (*op cit*) found that it is more difficult for parents to answer their children's questions about death and dying than their questions about sex, birth and contraception. This book has explored some of the ways in which communities based on relational principles can support families following a bereavement. Such communities are slowly dying out and the informal systems of support that they provided are disappearing with them. Instead, these are being replaced with professional support (Laungani, 1995). Although informal support may seem more 'homely' and 'natural' we should not condemn professional support. As discussed previously, the traditional principles born of experience on which such support systems were based does not automatically mean that they were effective for everyone. In addition, theory and research that brings together ideas from a wide range of perspectives and cultures, can inform professional practice and education so that such support systems are improved. The aim of this chapter is to introduce the reader to recent trends in the development of bereavement support for children, in particular death education and bereavement support groups.

Death education programs

Educators, health care professionals and many parents are becoming increasingly aware that protecting children from death can be damaging. Some are taking this further and arguing that death education should be incorporated into primary and secondary education about the complete life-cycle (Gordon and Klass, 1979; McNeil, 1984). Writers such as Gordon (1986) consider such incentives commendable, while others, such as Kitzinger and Kitzinger (1989) argue that care and thought needs to be given to the way in which such programs are implemented. Kitzinger and Kitzinger, although mainly supportive of death education in principle, expressed concern at the way in which some death education programs have been conducted in America. For example, children have been asked to make coffins and write their own wills. Kitzinger and Kitzinger report that, in America, the concept of death education has caused as much controversy as sex education did when this was introduced. However, most writers do appear to be supportive of the introduction of death education and this is one area in which the multidisciplinary team can make a valuable contribution.

Sometimes death education initiatives have been implemented because a child in the school has a terminal illness. It was the terminal illness of an eleven year old girl called Andrea, for example, which led Frierdich *et al* (1988) to develop a death education programme in collaboration with the child's school. Frierdich notes that cancer remains the leading cause of death in children in the USA. Many children, such as Andrea who fail to respond to treatment want to attend school for as long as they can. Kubler-Ross and Frierdich have both noted that terminally ill children are often quite honest about the fact that they are going to die and share this knowledge with their peers. In the case of Andrea, however, both her school teachers and friends found this very difficult to deal with. Therefore, Andrea's teachers asked the paediatric oncology staff (those who care for children with cancer) who were responsible for her care for help.

The outcome of this request was the development of a programme in collaboration with teachers at the school, nursing and medical staff from the hospital, the community mental health service, a social worker and a clergyman. Frierdich reports that the aim of the programme was as follows:

1. To encourage the children to express openly the fears and concerns which they had about death.

2. To provide information on rituals surrounding death and death terminology.

3.   To provide guidance on interaction with students who are dying.

4.   To provide counselling strategies and resource materials to school personnel and parents of classmates.

5.   To develop a support network for Andrea's class mates before and after her death.

The programme developed by the team took a holistic approach, dealing with the physiological aspects of death and dying. Information given to the children about the process of dying was presented in a descriptive and concrete way. This included discussion on the rhythm of breathing of a dying person, skin colour, nursing management and pain control. Information from this perspective on death, included telling the children that a dead person does not breathe, their heart does not beat and so forth.

Workshops in which the children were encouraged to discuss their feelings and fears about death and bereavement were added to the physiological aspects of the programme. During these workshops the children were told what kinds of feelings to expect, ie. anger, sadness, even pain. The children were also encouraged to discuss ways in which they could reconcile their emotions so that the grieving process could be facilitated rather than ignored. This included discussions of death rituals that, in turn, led the children to explore ways in which they could support each other following the death of Andrea, and of how they might remember her. When we consider that the child Andrea was involved in this initiative, it must have been strange for those involved, given that such things are not usually talked about, particularly in the presence of a dying child or adult. However, several writers have found that involvement in such discussions can be helpful to the dying child and to their peers (see *Chapter 4*).

The programme Frierdich developed for Andrea has grown and is provided for all the schools that a terminally ill child, who is cared for by the team, attends. The programme appears to be successful, but Frierdich cautions that several issues need to be clarified before the introduction and during the delivery of such an initiative. First, it is important to plan the programme carefully, ensuring that all involved have the necessary expertise to provide the contribution they will make. Thus, collaboration and a willingness to learn from each other is necessary for the professionals taking part in such a project. These professionals also need to confront their own feelings about death and bereavement before they encourage the children in their care to explore their feelings. Finally, Frierdich stresses the importance of informing children that not all patients who are diagnosed with cancer necessarily die from the disease.

In a sense death education is presented indirectly in the curriculum in most schools at primary school level when children are encouraged to categorise things that are alive, dead and have never lived. However, collaboration between education and health professionals, and the resultant holistic program such as that provided by Frierdich is still very much the exception rather than the norm. Indeed, even Frierdich's programme is only provided when a school has to deal with a terminally ill child and it is not a part of the standard curriculum in the United Kingdom. But there is potential for further research.

Support for bereaved children

Intellectual and emotional development can lead to variations in children's reactions to a bereavement. Thus, it is difficult to provide clear cut guidelines on the best method of supporting a bereaved child. The parent or caregiver faces significant pain in breaking the news to the child that a death has occurred. Following the death of a parent and, given that the surviving parent may be very distressed and disorientated due to his/her own sense of grief, this complicates the situation even further. As Hemmings (1995) noted:

> *'The surviving parent is distanced from the child by the depth of their grief and made less available to her because of how other people think she should behave. At the very time when the child needs more reassurance and love, she is told to want less.'*

It is not surprising that a bereaved child can perceive the world as a confusing and fragile place. Children exist in the context of a family, although people's concepts about what constitutes a family vary considerably. Anything that affects the significant others, can influence the child in both positive and negative ways. This is why Wells (*op cit*) argues that, if a parent dies and the surviving caregiver is too distressed to inform the child, another, more emotionally composed relation, friend or carer might be the more appropriate person to do this.

When breaking the news, Wells stresses the importance of recognising the individuality of the child and she emphasises the importance of touch and honesty. Touch, ie. taking the child into yours arms, conveys a sense of security, empathy and compassion, all of which help the child to feel loved. Given that children can be very unpredictable in their responses to the news of a death, Wells also stresses the importance of 'playing it by ear', of being honest and of telling the child that the deceased person loved him/her. Reassurance should also be given that the death is through no fault of the child.

When breaking the news of a death to a child, it is important that the person undertaking this task has all the facts, as these are known (Dyregrow and Kingsley, 1991). With younger children below the ages of ten or eleven, it is advisable to first tell the child to prepare for some bad news. Then, the news breaker should take a direct approach using plain English, eg. 'your mother has died, it was an accident' (Dyregrow and Kinglsey, 1991; Stewart and Dent, 1994). Dyregrow also explains that it may be necessary to discuss with the child, again in simple terms, what dead means, ie. the deceased's heart has stopped beating, he/she is no longer breathing, does not feel and is not aware of anything.

Although the child may find attendance at the funeral and viewing the body helpful, Dyregrow advises that a detailed explanation and description should be given in advance so that the child knows what to expect. Such explanations should include a description of the room, body and coffin. The child should also be told that other people attending the funeral will be very upset and should be reassured that it is permissible to express and share emotions.

The above advice is useful in that it may help readers to support a child during the initial stages up to and following the funeral of the deceased. But the process of grieving takes much longer than this. It is important not to assume that because adequate explanations have been given and the child has attended the funeral, that this is all the support that is necessary. Long-term support can be provided by the child's caregiver, but there is much to be said for additional professional support, particularly if the caregiver is also grieving.

In recent years, various groups and organisations, such as Cruise, Rainbows and the Compassionate Friends, have started to develop age-appropriate support to help children who have suffered a bereavement. Bereavement support can take the form of one-to-one therapy or group support. Sometimes, support groups are sponsored by large organisations and implemented by trained counsellors. In other cases, groups of education and health professionals form a multidisciplinary team which works together to develop death education and bereavement support groups (Ingram and Bernard, 1994; Hughes, *op cit*). There are similarities between support groups and death education programmes in that both provide information which enables children of different ages to understand death and bereavement. In doing this, death education programmes can act as a form of support for children but, generally, bereavement support groups have been developed to help specific groups of bereaved children.

A useful account of bereavement support groups currently available and advice on setting these up, can be found in Hughes (*op cit*). The next section considers some of the approaches developed by practitioners involved in setting up such groups. The aim of these approaches has been to help children understand the concept of death and feelings associated with bereavement, and to provide a safe and supportive environment in which to express such feelings. The section ends with a description of a support group developed by a group of health care practitioners in New Zealand. Finally, the section considers one-to-one support.

Hughes explains that bereavement support groups vary in their approach, some are designed for children of a specific age while others cater for children of all ages. The commonality between them is that group discussion is facilitated, using methods such as art or drama therapy. The aim of these methods is to encourage children to bring their feelings out into the open so that these can be dealt with in a supportive, caring environment. Although recognising the value of such groups, Hughes cautions that, as is the case with death education programmes, they need to be well planned and implemented by trained people who have themselves, confronted their own feelings about death and bereavement. The group leaders set the agenda and work closely with parents. Most bereavement support groups try to meet on a regular basis, ie. monthly. Hughes suggests that, since running such support groups uses considerable energy, it is wise to limit sessions to an hour at a time.

Given the limitations in young children's understanding (see *Chapter 1*) it seems clear that, until most children reach the Formal Operational Stage (12 years upward), they usually have difficulty in understanding the world in abstract terms. It is also difficult for them to express abstract feelings, so help will be needed to overcome this problem. Methods have been developed, by the facilitators of bereavement support groups, to help children express the abstract emotions associated with grief in a more concrete way. Hughes (*op cit*) for example, suggests that the group can be encouraged to draw a pepperoni pizza, which then grows smaller as it is eaten. Alternatively, the group can be asked to draw the ripples which are caused by a pebble thrown into the water. Having radiated out from where the pebble entered the water, when the ripples reach the limit of their outward movement, they begin to return to the centre. This can help, symbolically, to represent not only grief, and the way this feeling can grow during the first few months after bereavement, but also the way in which such painful feelings subside over time. The child can also be asked to indicate where, in the cycle of ripples, or stage of disposal of the pizza, they are in their grief.

Other strategies, described by Hughes, include encouraging the child to write a letter to the deceased, which he or she can then discuss with the rest of the group. Children in the group can be encouraged to draw a tree without leaves, to which paper leaves are added, each one representing the child's sources of emotional support. Drama can be used. Hughes gives the example of a 'feelings' game in which children can be urged to write down their feelings. The child can then act out these feelings in front of the other children of the group, and the latter can try to guess what these feelings are. All of these strategies help the child to name feelings and emotions that are difficult to articulate. This is most important because a child cannot begin to express his/her grief if she/he has no way of naming his/her feelings. Having found a way of admitting such feelings, the child can then be assured that to experience them is a natural part of the grieving process and, although the sense of regret at losing the person he/she cared about may never disappear, the intensity of the emotions will subside over time.

A moving and interesting account of how one such bereavement group was implemented is given in Ingram and Bernard's paper 'Helping children grieve' (1994). This article presents an account of how the authors, two New Zealand nurses, set the initiative for the development of a bereavement support group in the hospital in which they worked. The team who implemented the support group consisted of a play therapist, a paediatric nurse, a paediatric social worker and a midwife. The four sessions, which ran over two months, were developed by the team involved for a group of young children between six to twelve years of age. The professional team members involved the parents as much as possible, by giving them an account of what had been done during each of the sessions. Details of follow-up work was also provided so that parents could continue the sessions with their child.

Various methods were used during the meetings to encourage the young participants to express and explore their feelings. This included art therapy, in which the children drew a picture of their dead sibling, and then they discussed this with the rest of the group. The technique of storytelling, ie. a child wrote a story which he/she then shared with the group, was also used. One of the nurses, who had been trained in the skill of clowning appeared as Flip the Clown during some of the sessions. Presenting herself in this way, the nurse used mime, simulation of a bereavement (the death of Flip's doll Tommy) and drama as sources which encouraged the children to confront and act or talk out their feelings. At the concluding meeting, each child planted a shrub in memory of their dead sibling.

The children taking part in these sessions reaped the benefits of support not only from their parents and the health team involved, but also from each other. Peer group support is another issue that is of importance when considering the needs of bereaved children. The behaviour of significant others, such as the surviving parents, will be influenced by their ability to come to terms with their own sense of grief. Bereavement support, at an individual level for parents and children, which takes account of both short- and long-term considerations is important. As in all bereavement, the nature of the relationship between the bereaved and the deceased, and the context in which the death occurred will influence the nature of the support provided. In the case of the death of a sibling due to a stillbirth, for example, midwives are becoming increasingly sensitive to the needs of families and are providing photographs of the dead child (sometimes with the family) if the parents and siblings want this. Smith (1995) acknowledges that not all such families will want a photograph of their dead child. Nevertheless, she advises the nurse or midwife to take one to store in the notes, in case the parents later change their minds. Smith gives useful advice about precautions before taking the photograph. She recommends that care should be taken to place the dead child in a position that suggests that he or she is sleeping. Every effort should be made to arrange the setting to avoid inclusion of a 'clinical' background.

Individual long-term therapy or bereavement support can be very expensive. But some of the ideas suggested by Hemmings (1995) could be used by an understanding and supportive adult to encourage a bereaved child to discuss his/her feelings. Indeed, some of these strategies have to be used by parents and other caregivers in addition to professional people, otherwise some children would never receive any form of support. Hemmings suggests that visual imagery provided by commonplace household objects can be very useful in encouraging a child to talk about his/her feelings. The use of a snowstorm can help the child talk through how circumstances were settled before a bereavement, then disrupted (illustrated by shaking the snowstorm) and slowly, to outward appearances, return to normal. The child is, however, still aware that nothing will ever be the same again.

Both Hemmings and Lendrum and Syme (1992) have found that encouraging children to draw faces or make masks as a means of expressing emotions can be useful. Lendrum and Syme note that when children are encouraged to do this, the facilitator should observe the language that the child uses. If a child draws a 'bored' face, for example, this could mean not boredom but sadness or depression. When children suffer bereavement, they may find it difficult to know to which adults or other children they can turn to for help. Hemmings has developed a 'trust' game to help children overcome this problem. During the trust game, the child is encouraged to draw in the centre of a circle, an image of him/herself. The child is then encouraged to draw images of those closest to him/her, then second closest and so on. In this way, the child can identify for him/herself, sources of emotional support within the family or social group.

Workers have pointed out that it is very important for a bereaved child, especially in the case of the loss of a parent, to have a balanced memory of the deceased. If this is neglected, the child can build up an idealised memory of the deceased that can interfere in the future with the forming of attachments to alternative caregivers.

To overcome this problem, Hemmings uses a pair of old-fashioned weighing scales. The child is encouraged to write down all of the good memories of times shared with the deceased. As the child places each of these memories on the scales, he or she is encouraged to talk about the good memories. After several weeks the child is then encouraged to write down some of the less pleasant memories that he/she had of the deceased and these, again accompanied by discussion, are placed on the scales.

This is one game that should only be used by a professional working with a bereaved child. A person who does not have the necessary training may find that the child uncovers some quite painful memories and the supporter of the bereaved child could be placed in a situation that he/she is ill equipped to resolve. Hemmings emphasises that, even in the case of a professional, the game should be done very slowly, over several weeks. The therapist needs to work at the child's pace in order to discuss the memories recalled very thoroughly before moving on to the next.

It seems from the available evidence that both death education and bereavement support, at an individual and group level can be very helpful in helping children recover from a bereavement. Collaboration between caregivers seems to be very important, because no one person is equipped to help a bereaved child or group of bereaved children. From discussions in some sections of this book, it may appear that professional support would be unnecessary if communities and families provided support as they had in 'the good old days'. But professional support is guided by research and research tries to isolate the aspects of community support which are most useful. Further, it appears from the limited data collected for this study that, although community support can be helpful in the days before a funeral, it often disappears afterwards. Since grieving takes a long time, without long-term support, benefits afforded by death rituals and funerals can be quickly lost. However, despite the advantages that could be gained from collaborative support between professionals and informal caregivers, implementation of such schemes cost money.

Given the increasing cutbacks in welfare provision, it seems unlikely that bereavement support, such as that discussed in this chapter will be developed and implemented. This is unfortunate for the bereaved children who may be suffering and may continue to suffer unnecessarily. In the long-term, when considering the effects that unresolved grief can have in terms of the cost to society of treating mental health problems, ie. depression and social problems, it would be economically sound as well as humanitarian to provide such support as a right for all who have experienced a bereavement.

More research is needed, as is further development in the practice of both death education programs and bereavement support groups. The higher the numbers of parents, teachers, academics and health care professionals who take an interest in this area, the greater is the chance that funding for such development will be made available. We hope that in some small way, this book may promote such an interest.

References

Ainsworth MDS, Blehar MC, Waters E, Wall S (1978) *Patterns of Attachment: A Psychological Study of the Strange Situation.* Lawrence Erlbaum Associates, Hillsdale NT

Alteg T (1986) Death themes in adolescent music. In: Corr AC, Mcneil MC, eds. *Adolescence and Death.* Springer Publishing, New York

Anderson J, Bonnie S, Zinsser P (1988) *A History of their own: Women in Europe from Pre-History to the Present Time.* Penguin, Harmondsworth

Anthony S (1971) *The Discovery of Death in Childhood and After.* Penguin Education, Middlesex

Aries P (1974) *Western Attitudes Towards Death.* John Hoskins University Press, London

Ashton J (1982) Hitler did us a favour. In: Childs P, Wharton D, eds. *Children in War.* Institute of German, Austrian and Swiss Affairs, Nottingham University

Baldwinson D (1996) Reading War. Unpublished paper presented to The Health Sciences Health Research Interest Group, March 1996, South Bank University, London

Bandura A (1973) *Aggression: A Social Learning Analysis.* Prentice Hall, Englewood Cliffs, NJ

Bandura A (1980) The stormy decade: fact or fiction? In: RE Muss, ed. *Adolescent Behaviour and Society: A Book of Readings,* 3rd edn. Nardon House, New York: cited by Gordon (1986)

Becker C (1991) *Living and Relating: An Introduction to Phenomenology.* Sage, London

Bee H (1985) *The Developing Child.* Harper & Row, USA

Bergan M (1958) Effects of severe trauma on a four year old child. *Psychoanal Stud Child* **13**: 407–29

Bonnie S, Zinsser P (1988) *A History of Their Own: Women in Europe from Pre-History to the Present Time.* Penguin, Harmondsworth

Bowlby J (1969) *Attachment.* Basic Books, New York

Bowlby J (1979) Lecture 5. In: *The Making and Breaking of Affectional Bonds.* Tavistock Publications, London,

Bowlby J (1980) *Attachment and Loss: Vol 3: Loss, Sadness and Depression.* Penguin, Harmondsworth

Brown GW, Harris T (1978) *Social Origins of Depression.* Tavistock Publications, London

Cairns E (1992) Psychological research in Northern Ireland and the Troubles. *Psychologist* **5**: 341

Childs D (1982) The mass media influence. In: Childs D, Wharton D, eds. *Children in War*. Institute of German, Austrian and Swiss Affairs, Nottingham University

Clark AN, Clark AD (1976) *Early Experience, Myth and Evidence*. Open Books, London

Corr AC, McNeil MC (1986) *Adolescence and Death*. Springer Publishing, New York

Crase D (1980) The health educator as death educator: Professional preparation and quality control. *J School Health* **10**: 568–71

De Beauvoir S (1959) *Memoirs of a Dutiful Daughter*. Penguin, Harmondsworth

De Beauvoir S (1964) *A Very Easy Death*. Penguin, Harmondsworth

Dixon D (1989) The two faces of death: children's magazines and their treatment of death in the ninteenth century. In: Houlbrook R, ed. *Death, Ritual and Bereavement*. Routledge, London

Douglas J (1989) *Behaviour Problems in Young Children*. Tavistock and Routledge, London

Dyregrow A, Kingsley J (1991) *Grief in Children: A Handbook for the Professionals*. Jessica Kingsley Publishers, London

Dyregrow A, Livanga J, Mugisha C (1987) Children and War. Paper presented at the Third Annual Meeting of the Society for Trauma Stress studies, Baltimore, 23–26 October

Elizer R, Kaufman A (1983) Factors influencing the severity of childhood bereavement reactions. *Orthopsychiat* **53**: 668–76

Finke LM, Birenhaum LK, Chand N (1994) Two weeks post death report by parents of siblings' grieving experience. *J Child Adolesc Psychiat Nurs* **7**(4): 17–25

Fitzgerald H (1992) *The Grieving Child: A Parent's Guide*. Simon and Schuster, New York

Freud S (1961) Jokes and their relation to the unconscious. In: Strockey S, ed. *The Complete Psychological Works of Sigmund Freud*: Vol 8. Hogarth Press, London

Frierdich S, Urban A, Possin P, Ledman J (1988) The development of a program to assist school age children cope with the death of a classmate. In: Gilmore A, Gilmore S, eds. *A Safer Death: Multidisiplinary Aspects of Terminal Care*. Plenum Press, London

Furman R (1964) Death and the young child. *Psychoanal Stud Child* **19**: 329–32

Gillingham C (1993) Who is speaking/Who is listening? Creating a relational psychology. Unpublished paper presented at the

Discourse Psychology Conference, Psychoanalysis, Psychology and Masculinity, March 6th 1993, Manchester Metropolitan University, Manchester

Gilmore A, Gilmore S, eds, (1988) *A Safer Death: Multidisiplinary Aspects of Terminal Care*. Plenum Press, London

Gordon AK (1986) The tattered cloak of immortality. In: Corr AC, McNeil MC *Adolescence and Death*. Springer Publishing Company, New York

Gordon AK, Klass D (1979) *They Need to Know: How to Teach Children about Death*. NJ Prentice Hall, Englewood Cliffs

Gorer G (1965) *Death, Grief and Mourning in Contemporary Britain*. Cresset Press, London

Hall S *et al* (1921) *Aspects of Child Life and Education*. Penguin, Harmondsworth

Hemmings P (1995) Communicating with children through play. In: Smith SC, Pennells M, eds. *Interventions with Bereaved Children*. Jessica Kingsley Publishers, London and Bristol

Higgins R (1993) Hate in nursery rhymes: Captive audience, essential message. In Varma V, ed. *How and Why Children Hate*. Jessica Kingsley, London

Holland S (1975) Adolescents and politics: the student revolution. In: Meyerson S, ed. *Adolescence: The Crisis of Adjustment*. A Study of Adolescence by Members of the Tavistock Clinic and Other British Experts. Allen & Unwin, London

Hughes M (1995) *Bereavement and Support: Healing in a Group Environment*. Taylor & Frances, Bristol

Isaacs S (1930) *The Social Development of Young Children*. Penguin, Harmondsworth

Ingram P, Bernard J (1994) Helping Children Grieve. *Nursing* **2**(7): 12–14

Jewett C (1984) *Helping Children Cope with Separation and Loss*. Batsford, London

Kahns M (1982) God help us if we lose. In: Childs D, Wharton D, eds. *Children in War*. Institute of German, Austrian and Swiss Affairs, University of Nottingham

Kapp S (1976) *If You Meet the Buddha on the Road, Kill Him*! Bantam, New York

Kastenbaum R (1967) The child's understanding of death: How does it develop? In: Grallman EA, ed. *Explaining Death to Children*. Beacon Publishing, Boston

Kastenbaum R (1986) Death in the world of adolescence. In: Corr AC, McNeil MC, eds. *Adolescence and Death*. Springer Publishing, New York

Kastenbaum RL (1988) Safe death in the post modern world. In: Gilmore A, Gilmore S, eds. *A Safer Death: Multidisciplinary Aspects of Terminal Care*. Plenum Press, London

Kenny C *et al* (1998a) *A Northern Thanatology*. Quay Books, Dinton

Kenny C *et al* (1998c) *Thanatology of War*. Quay Books, Dinton

Kitzinger S, Kitzinger C (1989) *Talking with Children About Things that Matter*. Pandora, London

Klein M (1960) *Our Adult World and its Roots in Infancy*. Tavistock Publishing, London

Kubler-Ross E (1969) *On Death and Dying*. Macmillan Publishing, New York

Kubler-Ross E (1983) *On Children and Death*. Macmillan Publishing, New York

Lansdown R (1987) The development of the concept of death. *Curr Iss Clin Psychol* **8**: 2

Laungani P (1995) Is psychotherapy bad for your health. *Br Assoc Couns* **6**(2): 110–215

Laungani P (1996) Patterns of bereavment in Indian and British culture. *Bereavment Care* **14**(1): 5–7

Laungani P (1997) Death in a Hindu family. In: Parkes CM, Laungani P, Young B eds. *Death and Bereavement Across Cultures*. Routledge, London

Lendrum S, Syme G (1992) *The Gift of Tears: A Practical Approach to Loss and Bereavment Counselling*. Routledge, London

Littlewood J (1992) *Aspects of Grief: Studies of Bereavement in Adult Life*. Routledge, London

Lundin T (1984) Long-term outcome of bereavement. *Br J Psychiatry* **144**: 424–28

McCown DE (1984) Funeral attendance, cremation and young siblings. *Death Educ* **8**: 349–63

Miles AI (1990) Caring for families when a child dies. *Pediatr Nurs* **16**(4): 346–57

Miles MS (1985) Helping adults mourn the death of a child. *Iss Comprehen Paediatr Nurs* **8**(1–6): 219–41

Molnar-Skiklers L (1985) Effect of a brief instructional unit on education in death: attitudes of prospective teachers. *J Social Health* **55**: 6

Morgan (1994) Cited by Stewart A, Dent A. *At a Loss: Bereavement Care When a Baby Dies*. Balliere Tindall, London

Nagy M (1959) The child's view of death. In: Fiefel H, ed. *The Meaning of Death*. McGraw-Hill, New York

Parkes CM (1970) Seeking and finding a lost object: evidence from recent studies of the reactions to bereavement. *Social Sci Med* **4**: 187–207

Parkes CM (1972) *Bereavement: Studies of Grief in Adult Life*. Routledge, London

Parkes CM, Laungani P, Young B eds. (1997) *Death and Bereavement Across Cultures*. Routledge, London

Peetz D (1982) Not unfortunately a Corporal Von Stauffenberg. In: Childs D, Wharton D. *Children at War*. Institute of German, Austrian and Swiss Affairs, University of Nottingham

Piaget J (1932) *The Moral Judgment of the Child*. Macmillan, New York

Piaget J (1952) *The Origins of Intelligence in Children*. International Universities Press, New York

Pincus L (1974) *Death and the Family*. Panthon, New York

Pojman LP (1992) *Life and Death: Grappling with the Moral Dilemmas of Our Time*. Jones and Bartlett Publishing, London

Roberts E (1989) The Lancashire way of death. In: Houlbrook R, ed. *Death, Ritual and Bereavement*. Routledge, London

Rochlin G (1967) How younger children view death and themselves. In: Grollman BA, ed. *Explaining Death to Children*. Beacon Press, Boston

Smith SE, Pennells M (1995) *Interventions with Bereaved Children*. Jessica Kingley Publications, London and Bristol

Soineta JJ, Rigler D, Karen M (1973) Anxiety in the dying child. *Paediatrics* **52**: 841

Stewart A, Dent A (1994) *At a Loss: Bereavement Care When a Baby Dies*. Balliere Tindall, London

Terr L (1983) Chowchilla revisited: the effects of psychic trauma four years after a school-bus kidnapping. *Am J Psychol* **15**: 43

Turner B, Rennell T (1995) *When Daddy Came Home: How Family Life Changed Forever in 1945*. Hutchinson UK, London

Trew K (1992) Social psychological research on the conflict. *Psychologist* **5**: 342–4

Van de Zand W (1989) Witness to an invasion. In: Childs d, Wharton J eds. Children in War. Institute of German, Austrian and Swiss Affairs, University of Nottingham, Nottingham

Van-Eerdewegh MM *et al* (1985) The bereaved child. *Br J Psychol* **140**: 23–9

Weller EB, Weller RA, Fristad MA (1988) Should children attend their parents funerals? *J Am Acad Child Adolesc Psychol* **27**: 559–62

Wells R (1990) *Helping Children Cope With Death Facing a Death in the Family*. Sheldon Press, London

Wilson R, Cairns E (1992) Stress, trouble and psychological disorder in Northern Ireland. *Psychologist* **5**: 347–50

Worden JW (1991) *Grief Counselling and Grief Therapy*. Springer, New York

Yorder L (1994) Comfort and consolidation: a nurse's perspective on parental bereavement. *Pediatric Nurs* **20**(5): 7: Women's Children's Service, Memorial Mission, Ashelle (NC)

Yule W (1989) The effects of disasters on children. *Newsletter, Assoc Child Psychol Psychiatry* **11**(6): 3–6

Index